Beginner's Guide to Electric Wiring

Beginner's Guides are available on the following subjects:

Audio
Tape Recording
Radio
Television
Colour Television
Computers
Electronics
Transistors
Integrated Circuits
Electric Wiring
Domestic Plumbing
Central Heating
Woodworking

Beginner's Guide to Electric Wiring

F Guillou
Lecturer in Electrical Engineering,
Old Swan Technical College, Liverpool

C Gray, BSc
Lecturer in Electrical Engineering,
Old Swan Technical College, Liverpool

Newnes Technical Books

The Butterworth Group

United Kingdom	Butterworth & Co (Publishers) Ltd London: 88 Kingsway, WC2B 6AB
Australia	Butterworths Pty Ltd Sydney: 586 Pacific Highway, Chatswood, NSW 2067 Also at Melbourne, Brisbane, Adelaide and Perth
Canada	Butterworth & Co (Canada) Ltd Toronto: 2265 Midland Avenue, Scarborough, Ontario M1P 4S1
New Zealand	Butterworths of New Zealand Ltd Wellington: 77—85 Customhouse Quay 1, CPO Box 472
South Africa	Butterworth & Co (South Africa) (Pty) Ltd Durban: 152—154 Gale Street
USA	Butterworth (Publishers) Inc Boston: 10 Tower Office Park, Woburn, Mass. 01801

First published 1965
Second edition 1975
Reprinted 1976
Reprinted 1977
Reprinted 1979

© Butterworth & Co (Publishers) Ltd 1965, 1975

ISBN 0 408 00157 7

Printed in England by
The Whitefriars Press Limited
London and Tonbridge

PREFACE

THIS book is intended to bridge the gap between the layman and electrical tradesman, with regard to electric wiring in homes and workshops. Although the work is not intended as a textbook for students, the information given complies with the 14th Edition of the IEE Regulations for the Electrical Equipment of Buildings, and much of the content will be useful to first year electrical students in the electrical contracting industry. The reader need not have any technical knowledge at the start. Only simple calculations are involved.

The authors emphasise the need for adequate and safe electrical wiring in the home, as too often death and injury result from unsafe electrical installations. It is hoped that this book will reduce the number of dangerous situations arising out of the layman's mistaken understanding of the correct methods of electrical wiring.

F.G.
C.G.

CONTENTS

1

INTRODUCTION

THE purpose of electric wiring is to make available electrical energy whenever it is required:

(a) With maximum safety.

(b) With the proper capability of supplying the current for the usage required and for possible future extended usage.

(c) With maximum reliability.

(d) With maximum flexibility to provide for change in usage and extension.

(e) At minimum cost.

TERMINOLOGY

Terms used throughout this book include the following:

Wiring. The fixed installation of insulated electric cables between the intake point in a particular installation and the appliances that use the current (such as lamps, radiators, cookers, radio sets, etc.), including the fuses, switches, socket-outlets, lampholders and all other parts permanently fixed in the building.

Appliances. All current-consuming apparatus, whether fixed (such as a plumbed-in water heater), or portable (such as an electric iron).

Socket-outlet. A properly designed and permanently fixed device installed so that a portable appliance can be safely plugged in. (In Britain, although not in some other countries, all socket-outlets should be of the three-pin type, with two pins for the circuit connections and one for the earth connection.)

Area Electricity Board. In Britain, all electricity supplies are given by one or other of the twelve Area Electricity Boards (in England and Wales) and equivalent authorities in Scotland. For the purposes of this book, the term ' Area Board ' may be taken as referring to the electricity supply authority, whether it is a Board, a power company, or any other body.

Series connection. A form of connection in which all the current passes through the circuits or appliances one after the other.

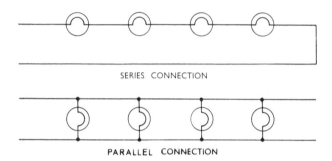

SERIES CONNECTION

PARALLEL CONNECTION

Parallel connection. A form of connection in which all current-consuming parts of the circuit are individually connected across the two live wires providing the supply.

POWER SUPPLY

The source of power and the circuit principle

Electricity is generated in power stations where coal or oil is burnt to produce steam which turns a turbine coupled to an electrical generator. In Britain a number of power stations in which nuclear energy—power from the atom—is used are now providing power, the heat from the atomic reaction serving the same purpose as burning fuel in the furnace. In Britain there is a small proportion of power generated by falling water, driving a water-wheel, or water turbine, but in some countries the majority of the power supply comes from this source.

The power is almost universally generated as alternating current, where the direction of flow of current changes fifty times a second. In America and in some other parts of the world, the frequency, or number of direction changes is 60 hertz. Alterna-

ting current is used in preference to direct current mainly for
ease of transforming from high to low voltage, and vice versa.

Obviously, the more current that is needed the larger the
conductor necessary at a given pressure. This can be understood
by reference to a water pipe system. To fill a given tank in a
given time, two methods can be used. Either a high-pressure
hose, of small diameter, can be employed, or else a low pressure
and a large hose. It is the same with electricity, where the
pressure is represented by the voltage, and the flow by the
current. To carry large amounts of power from power stations
perhaps fifty or one hundred miles away from the point of consumption, overhead grid systems are used. It would be impossible to increase the size of electrical conductor carried on pylons
beyond a certain practical limit. The only way, then, to carry
more power, is to increase the pressure, or voltage.

By the use of the transformer, which will be mentioned later
in this book, alternating current can be transformed up or down
in pressure, as required, and the pressure used for bulk trans-
mission on the grid system is as high as 750,000 volts.

This power is transformed down until it reaches the transformer
at the end of one's own street, or somewhere on an industrial or
housing estate site, at a pressure of 11,000 volts; and the final
transformation, to feed the power into the cables connected to the
consumer's premises, is to a pressure of 415/240 volts, 3-phase.

All alternating current power is generated on the 3-phase
system. This means that the part of the generator where the
rotating magnetic field sets up the current we ultimately use is
divided into three equal sectors, for practical reasons of better
utilisation of the materials in the generator. The three separate
windings, in which the power is generated, are brought out by
means of six wires, one at the end of each winding, and one end
of each winding has the wires connected to a common point,
known as the neutral. The other ends—the free ends—are the
supply mains, usually known as phases, and for ease of identification, called in Britain, the red, yellow and blue phases.

The 3-phase system continues all the way to the transformer
near to the consumer's premises, which we will call the local

transformer, and on the low voltage side of this transformer we thus have four wires, the red, yellow and blue phases and the neutral. These wires are usually coloured or identified with red, yellow and blue markings, with black for the neutral (Fig. 1.1).

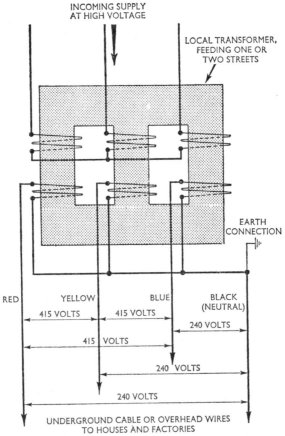

FIG. 1.1. The transformer that steps down the high voltage supplies from the power station, near to the consumer's premises and provides a 3-phase supply.

In the 3-phase system, two voltages exist. Between each phase and the neutral wire, on the low voltage side of the local transformer, the voltage is 240 volts, the standard voltage in Britain (in other countries this may differ, and in America, for example, 110 volts is commonly used). But between the red and yellow phases there is a voltage of 415 volts, and 415 volts also exists between the yellow and blue, and between the blue and red. This is the reason why the output voltage of the local transformer is given as 415/240 volts.

The cables running out from the local transformer to the premises of the consumer (usually underground, but in rural districts overhead, on wooden poles) are tapped off, for each house, by taking a connection, say for the first house in the street from the red phase wire in the 3-phase cable and from the neutral, thus giving a 240 volt supply to that house; for the second house, from the yellow phase wire and the neutral; and for the third house from the blue phase wire and the neutral.

This form of connection is made in order to balance the demand on the three phases, since the generator must ultimately supply a balanced load, and the varying demands of the thousands of consumers that might be connected to any one generator will balance out if connections are made in this way (Fig. 1.2).

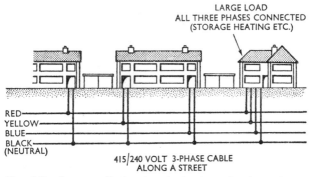

FIG. 1.2. System of balancing the loads on the three phases in a suburban street.

However, it is usual, where the demand in a particular consumer's premises exceeds 15 kilowatts, for a 3-phase supply to be given, because the load would be too great to be balanced out properly if connected only to a single phase. Therefore more and more consumers, including private houses, are being fed with a 3-phase supply, as the loads grow.

At the local transformer, the neutral connection of the low voltage side, that feeds the consumers, is connected to earth. But this does not mean that the neutral wire must be considered as safe. There are circumstances under which it could become alive, and although in general the neutral (black) connection appears to be at the same voltage as the general mass of earth, it must at all times be treated as a live wire. The neutral wire is *not* the earth connection, to which reference will be made later, except in special circumstances, which will be mentioned later under Protective Multiple Earthing (see p. 77).

Non-standard systems

What has been said above applies to the vast majority of electrical installations in Britain and most other countries. But it must not be forgotten that there are still some non-standard installations, even in the British Isles.

(i) *Direct current supply*. In a few cases, direct current, usually at 220 volts, is supplied. In this case, all the fuses and switches used must be suitable for this system, as the act of breaking a direct current system produces different effects from those associated with alternating current, for example with regard to prolonging the spark, or arc, created at the switch blades.

Care must be taken to ensure that all appliances used are suitable for direct current. Many appliances are not suitable for d.c. use, for example, most machines such as refrigerators (that are fitted with motors), or washing machines, cannot be used on d.c.

(ii) *Non-standard alternating current systems*. Some systems have non-standard voltages, such as 210 volts, or even 105 volts, and a few others have non-standard alternating current frequency, such as 25 hertz, or 33⅔ hertz. In these two cases, the wiring principles are not particularly affected, but all the appliances have to be chosen to be suitable for the special characteristics of the supply system (Fig. 1.3).

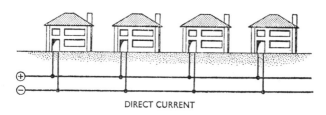

DIRECT CURRENT

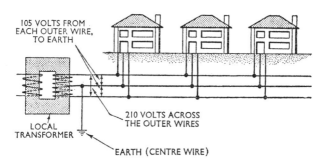

105 VOLTS FROM EACH OUTER WIRE, TO EARTH

210 VOLTS ACROSS THE OUTER WIRES

LOCAL TRANSFORMER

EARTH (CENTRE WIRE)

3-WIRE ALTERNATING CURRENT SYSTEM

FIG. 1.3. Two non-standard supply systems: *above,* direct current; *below,* 3-wire alternating current with centre point earthed.

THE CIRCUIT

It is fundamental to all forms of usage of electricity that there must be a circuit (see Fig. 1.4). This means that the current must be able to flow from the point where it originates, at the local transformer, on, say, the blue phase terminal, through the supply cable to the consumer's premises, through his wiring to the appliance, through the appliance, and back to the neutral

SIMPLEST TYPE OF ELECTRICITY SUPPLY SYSTEM —
A BATTERY FEEDS A LAMP

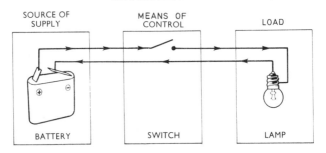

SOURCE OF
SUPPLY

MEANS OF
CONTROL

LOAD

BATTERY

SWITCH

LAMP

THE CIRCUIT IS FROM THE POSITIVE TERMINAL OF THE BATTERY
THROUGH THE SWITCH, THROUGH THE LAMP,
BACK TO THE NEGATIVE TERMINAL.

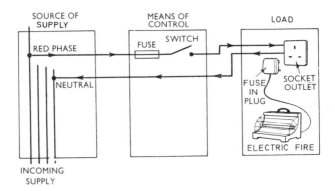

SOURCE OF
SUPPLY

MEANS OF
CONTROL

LOAD

RED PHASE

FUSE   SWITCH

NEUTRAL

FUSE
IN
PLUG

SOCKET
OUTLET

ELECTRIC FIRE

INCOMING
SUPPLY

THE CIRCUIT IS FROM THE LIVE PHASE OF THE SUPPLY,
THROUGH THE FUSE AND THE SWITCH, THROUGH THE
LOAD (ELECTRIC FIRE), VIA THE SOCKET OUTLET AND
BACK TO THE NEUTRAL CONDUCTOR OF THE SUPPLY MAIN.

FIG. 1.4. The principle of the electric circuit: *above*, the
simplest electrical circuit; *below*, the normal alternating
current circuit used on domestic premises.

connection and so back to the other end of the red phase wiring at the local transformer.

This is the fundamental point to be appreciated in all considerations of electrical wiring; there must be a circuit.

FUNDAMENTAL CONSIDERATIONS

Dealing now with the essential points concerning the purpose of electric wiring, we first touch on safety.

Safety

Electricity is a good servant but a dangerous master. The lowest recorded voltage at which death occurred from an electric shock is 38 volts. In general, 240 volts seldom kills a fully dressed person wearing dry footwear (but may do so): but it is a fatal voltage for anyone wearing damp shoe leather, or perhaps with bare feet standing on a damp floor or touching earth metal. The circuit, in this case, is from the live, or phase, conductor through the person's body and back to the earth point where the neutral connection is earthed in the local transformer. Since the whole mass of earth including all the buried metal and so on usually has very little resistance to the passage of current, the full current that could flow from the live wire through the person is limited only by the resistance offered by the person's body. Damp skin is a much better conductor than dry skin, and damp shoes offer very little insulation.

Anyone attempting to carry out electric wiring must at all times remember that he is dealing with a potentially lethal form of energy.

In Britain, it is still permissible for anyone to extend his or her electric wiring system, or to install new wiring, without special qualifications. In many other countries this is not the case. It is a punishable offence, for example, in New Zealand, for anyone other than a registered and qualified electrician to install wiring of any kind.

However, if the work is undertaken with a full sense of responsibility, proper materials are used and proper methods employed, there is no reason why a safe installation should not result. *But the person installing wiring should always have in the front of his mind the possibility that he might have to give evidence at a Coroner's Court.*

The safety of electrical appliances and wiring is ensured, basically, in three ways. First, by *insulation*; secondly, by *earthing*; and thirdly, *by proper protection against fire risk.*

Insulation

Insulation is the method whereby the live electric wires or other equipment is covered in such a way that it is impossible for anyone to come into contact with live metal. Wiring, for example, is made up of copper conductors (sometimes aluminium conductors) covered with rubber or with plastic or with some other substances for special purposes (such as asbestos-based materials), and if the right type of cable is used, there can be no danger from touching the outside of the insulating covering.

Appliances of all kinds, if of proper design, have the live parts completely encased in porcelain or plastic materials so that it is impossible even for an inquiring child to insert its finger into any part that is live, or else the live equipment exists inside a sealed part of the appliance, and access can only be obtained to it by deliberate interference.

Double insulation

Certain appliances are of what is known as the 'double-insulated' type. These appliances have first the normal funct-ional insulation, as in all other appliances, and then a separate protective insulation enclosing all metal parts. Such appliances do not need an earth connection, but it must be borne in mind that no appliance can be considered as double insulated unless it complies with the Regulations and has been certified by the British Electrical Approvals Board.

Some (but not all) designs of shavers, hair dryers, dishwashers, clocks, blankets and similar appliances have been certified as double insulated, and thus need only the live phase and the neutral connections to the mains.

Earthing

Earthing is the second line of defence. The whole mass of earth is obviously safe from the electrical point of view. Therefore if, say, a kettle has a wire connecting the body of the kettle, which can be touched, to the earth, then whatever happens to the live wires inside the kettle heating element, or in the connector

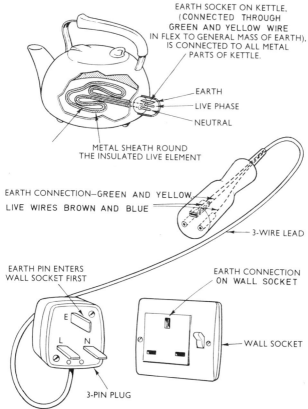

FIG. 1.5. The earthing of a portable appliance, showing the connection through the 3-wire flexible lead to the earth point on the socket-outlet.

feeding the appliance with current, the user is safe because any current finding its way to the body of the appliance would be short-circuited straight to earth (see Fig 1.5).

Metal parts of any kind of appliance in which electricity is used should always be earthed*. With portable appliances, this is carried out, as will be seen later, by using a 3-core flexible cable and a proper plug and socket-outlet, the third pin of which, the earth pin (separate and different from the live phase and neutral pins) is properly connected to the earth. This is done by running a wire directly from the socket-outlet on the wall to a proper earth point, which (by arrangement with the Area Electricity Board only) may be earthed lead sheathing of the supply cables at the consumer's terminal point, or may be a special earth prepared properly and provided for this purpose.

At the appliance end, the connector or the cable termination (if it is a fixed termination) must be so arranged that every metal part of the appliance is properly connected to a terminal to which the third wire in the flexible—green and yellow—is connected, so that whatever leakage of current might take place, in whatever part of the appliance, the current will flow harmlessly to the earth point, through the green and yellow wire into the plug and to earth via the proper earth point.

Protection against fire risk

Protection against fire risk is secured by using properly dimensioned cables and fittings, and by protecting the circuits by means of the correct sizes and types of fuses or circuit breakers.

Properly designed wiring

As well as the danger of shock, the supply of electric power from a large power station brings with it another danger.

When current passes through a wire, there is a certain resistance in the wire to be overcome. In overcoming this resistance, heat is generated in the wire. In the case of the ordinary open-type electric radiator, this heating effect is usefully employed to give the heat we require from the radiator.

* With the exception of properly certified double-insulated appliances, mentioned on page 18.

But heat is also being generated in the wiring itself. If the wiring is properly proportioned, the heating effect is small, but if the wire is not suitable, and the size employed is too small, two problems arise. First, in extreme cases there is danger of fire from the wiring becoming too hot, and setting fire to some adjacent materials such as wood shavings, and secondly some of the voltage in the supply mains will be lost in the cable itself, and the appliance will not receive its full voltage, and thus, for example, lights may be dimmer than they should be.

This question of the proper dimensioning of the wiring installation in relation to the load to be fed with current applies not only to the wiring itself but to all the appliances used. Even the ordinary switch found on the wall of a living room must be suitable for its duty. Poorly designed switches, or switches that have become worn out, cannot carry the current they were intended to carry, or the increased current that wiring extensions have made possible for them to carry, mainly because the contact parts within the switch were never large enough, or have become twisted or bent or overheated so that they no longer make good contact. In consequence, there is too high a resistance within the switch, further heat is generated, and fire may result. This factor also applies to fuses, to junction boxes and to any part of the installation such as lampholders. There is a special aspect of the fire risk to be borne in mind when lampholders are considered.

In these days, people have become accustomed to higher levels of lighting than were accepted in the past, and they have tended to add larger and larger lamps to existing lampholders. In addition, there are now available mushroom-shaped lamps which give a high wattage, or power consumption, in a small volume, and fittings for lighting purposes are being made to accommodate lamps of a greater power than those for which they were designed.

A lamp gives out almost the whole of its power consumption in the form of heat. The overheating which may take place when lamps that are too large for the appliances are used may give rise to serious consequences, because the flexible or other wiring connected to the lampholder may become overheated to the stage where its insulation is damaged, and a short circuit may occur which at the least may black out a number of lights, or at the most give rise to a fire.

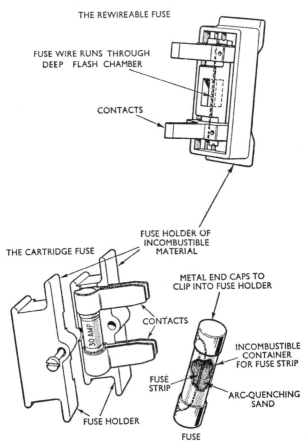

FIG. 1.6. Two types of fuse: *above*, the rewireable fuse; *below*, the cartridge fuse.

Protection of the installation

It is necessary also to consider the proper protection of the wiring installation. The most commonly used type of protection is the fuse (Fig. 1.6).

A fuse is like a weak link in a chain, carefully designed to break when the maximum permissible load is exceeded so that the crane, for example, to which a chain might be connected cannot be overloaded and perhaps overturned.

In the electric circuit, a fuse consists usually of a fine wire which has been carefully selected so that when the maximum current which the circuit should carry is exceeded the overload will cause the wire to melt and so act as a switch to open the circuit and cut off the current, so saving the wiring itself and all the appliances on the circuit from damage.

Fuses are usually contained in fuseholders and installed in a fuseboard, in such a way that the designed overheating of the fuse and its ultimate rupture by melting cannot give rise to any fire risk or other serious consequences.

The circuits in the installation must be fused according to the Regulations mentioned later, and care must be taken to see that if a fuse should blow it must be replaced with a fuse of the proper type for the duty required, and not with a larger type which would invalidate the protection it gives to the circuit.

It is extremely unwise to repair a fuse that has blown without finding out why it blew. It might well happen that the danger still exists, for example if a flexible cord is frayed through it may have shorted its two conductors together sufficiently to have blown the fuse, and then left the bare copper exposed, so that a shock could result if the fuse is replaced. The faulty part of the installation should either be repaired or temporarily isolated, before replacing the fuse that has blown.

Reliability

Since most of us rely entirely on our electrical systems, anyone installing any kind of wiring must be careful to ensure that the wiring is absolutely reliable. This means that not only must it be properly proportioned but that it must be laid out in the building in such a way that it is not likely to be subjected to casual damage, and that any failure of wiring, or of appliances connected to any particular circuit, must not be allowed to give rise to wholesale blackouts and failures of supply in other parts of the building.

Flexibility

Wiring requirements are constantly changing.   With the addition of more and more domestic appliances, for domestic users, and more and more electrical services in offices (for office machinery and every kind of mechanical aid to office working, together with increased lighting), while in small factories and workshops additional electrical appliances are constantly being added, thought should be given to planning the installation so that it does not become overloaded for want of additional wiring facilities, which the installation should allow for in the planning stage, so that they can be added easily at a later date and prevent overloading, with all its risks, taking place as the increase of load gradually builds up.

Minimum cost

There are many people who naturally feel that wiring must always be carried out as cheaply as possible.   It is safe to say that good wiring pays for itself in peace of mind and in ease and convenience of usage.   Money skimped on a wiring installation is money unwisely skimped.   The minimum cost consideration should never be in the forefront of the mind of anyone planning or executing a wiring installation.

THE ELECTRICIAN'S RESPONSIBILITY

In every installation, the Area Electricity Board (in Britain) or the Electricity Supply Company or Authority provides a service terminal point, on which all parts are sealed (see Fig. 1.7).   This usually consists of a main fuse, or cut-out, and a meter. Nowadays, more and more people are using off-peak current, with the supply to the water-heating or space-heating circuits being restricted to the off-peak hours, that occur during the night and sometimes

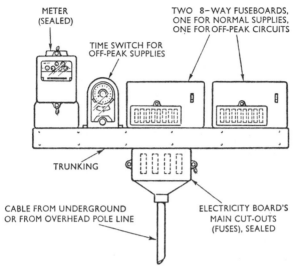

METER
(SEALED)

TIME SWITCH FOR
OFF-PEAK SUPPLIES

TWO 8–WAY FUSEBOARDS,
ONE FOR NORMAL SUPPLIES,
ONE FOR OFF-PEAK CIRCUITS

TRUNKING

CABLE FROM UNDERGROUND
OR FROM OVERHEAD POLE LINE

ELECTRICITY BOARD'S
MAIN CUT-OUTS
(FUSES), SEALED

FIG. 1.7. Consumer's terminal showing trunking to carry wiring to meters, fuseboards and time switch. (Note: if off-peak supplies are used, two meters will be required.)

during the afternoon period. If this type of usage is contemplated the Area Electricity Board will provide, in addition, a time switch to adjust the hours of usage of the off-peak current (which is usually supplied at about half the price of normal current), and a separate meter.

All these appliances are the property of the Area Board, and must not be interfered with in any way by the electrician. To break the seal on the main fuses or any part of the metering circuit is to invite prosecution.

After the meter, the responsibility for the installation lies entirely with the consumer, and if it is a new installation, the electrician is therefore responsible for handing over to the consumer a proper wiring installation, which the Area Electricity Board will test, and if found in good order will connect up to the meters.

THE ELECTRICIAN'S 'BIBLE'

The only official guide to electric wiring is the Wiring Regulations of the Institution of Electrical Engineers. The book, known as *Regulations for the Electrical Equipment of Buildings*, is available from the Institution (Savoy Place, London, W.C. 2), and these Regulations are constantly being amended, so that the user must make certain of providing himself with the latest copy.

These Regulations, although they are not part of the law of the land, are very nearly in the same category. For example, an insurance company, if it is asked to insure a building, will nearly always specify that the electrical wiring must be in conformity with the practice laid down in the Wiring Regulations of the Institution. In cases where accidents occur, such as fires or electrical shocks, the best possible defence, on the part of the person who installed the wiring, is that it is in conformity with the I.E.E. Regulations. One would have a very poor defence indeed if the wiring did not conform to the Regulations.

Tests by Area Electricity Board

In addition, the Area Electricity Board has the right to refuse to connect up an installation which it considers to be unsafe, and such an installation obviously does not comply with the Regulations. The tests the Board's Engineers will apply will be directed to ensuring that the Regulations have been properly carried out.

The Electricity Board also has the right to be consulted when any alteration or addition is made to an installation, and will inspect the altered or added parts before they are connected to the main system.

SOME DEFINITIONS

Voltage

The pressure that forces the current round an electric circuit is measured in volts. The normal domestic supply (on systems with standard supplies) is given at 240 volts: a flashlamp bulb works at 1·5 volts: most of the National Grid System works at

275,000 volts, parts at 400,000 volts. The voltage is equivalent to the head of water causing a flow along a pipe.

The Regulations define the following levels of voltage:

Extra-low voltage: below 50 volts.

Low voltage: not exceeding 250 volts.

Medium voltage: above 250 volts but not exceeding 650 volts.

The electrician, dealing with domestic and small industrial installations, will therefore deal mainly with low-voltage supplies, but, as mentioned earlier, the 415-volt supplies that are associated with 3-phase connections may bring his operations into the medium-voltage field.

Current

The flow, or current, in a conductor is measured in amperes. A one-bar radiator needs a flow of about 4·16 amperes: a 100-watt lamp needs about 0·4 amperes.

Resistance

When water flows through a thin pipe, it encounters a resistance to its flow. The larger the pipe, the less resistance. Also pipes differ, in resistance to flow, even at the same diameter. A smooth-bore pipe will offer less resistance than a rusted bore.

Similarly, with conductors of electricity, the thicker the wire, in general the less the resistance. Certain wires, like copper, silver and aluminium, have less resistance than that of similar-sized wires of steel or nickel alloy.

The effect of resistance

The effect of resistance in a conductor is to generate heat as the current passes, as mentioned earlier. In the case of radiator elements, this is the desired effect, and the conductors used in these elements are designed to give a suitable resistance to generate the required amount of heat.

But in the conductors used for wiring a house, the aim should always be to reduce this heating effect to the minimum. Heat is not required in the wiring system: it will reduce the life of the insulation, and if excessive may even cause a fire.

Therefore care must always be taken to reduce the heating effect to the minimum by ensuring that all conductors used—the cables themselves, and all the fittings of every kind—are large enough to present a very low resistance to the current for which the circuit is to be used.

Resistance is measured in ohms. As an example, a 100-watt lamp has a resistance of about 600 ohms (though this varies a little as it heats up).

The resistance of the insulation used on electrical appliances is of course very high indeed—otherwise it would not be regarded as insulation. To give a typical example, the resistance of the insulation used in a good, new electric iron, measured between the live conductors in the element and the outer metal case of the iron, ought to be about 2,000,000 ohms.

The resistance of all parts of an electrical installation in a domestic dwelling—that is, the resistance of all the live conductors in the cables, the switches, the socket-outlets, and the fuseboards—measured against earth, must not be less than 1,000,000 ohms, known as 1 *megohm*.

Later we shall see how this insulation resistance is tested.

TWO SIMPLE FORMULAE

There are two very simple and fundamental formulae that must be understood in relation to all electric circuits.

The ability of an appliance of any kind to consume electricity is measured in watts. A thousand watts equals one *kilowatt*.

An appliance that is so designed that its resistance allows 1 ampere of current to flow when the appliance is connected to a power source giving 1 volt is said to have a capacity of 1 watt.

Therefore:

$$\text{watts} = \text{amperes} \times \text{volts}.$$

As an example, a one-bar radiator with an element of 1000 watts (1 kilowatt) capacity, would take current as shown here, if connected to a 240-volt circuit:

$$\text{watts} = \text{amperes} \times \text{volts}$$
$$1000 = 4 \cdot 16 \times 240.$$

If you know any two of these three figures, you can calculate the other.

Often it is desired to know how many amperes will be needed to feed a certain appliance, say a television set with a nameplate that says ' 200 watts '. We proceed as follows, assuming the set is to be connected to the 240-volt supply mains:

$$watts = amperes \times volts.$$

Therefore:

$$\frac{watts}{volts} = amperes$$

$$\frac{200}{240} = \tfrac{5}{6} \text{ of an ampere, or } 0.83 \text{ ampere.}$$

Ohm's law

The relation between the voltage or pressure, and the current, or flow, in a simple circuit that has a certain resistance, is as follows:

$$\text{Current in amperes} = \frac{\text{Pressure in volts}}{\text{Resistance in ohms}}$$

To give a simple example, a kettle of 3 kilowatts rating will have resistance (in its heating element) calculated as follows:

$$watts = amperes \times volts.$$

Therefore:

$$\frac{watts}{volts} = amperes.$$

$$\frac{3000}{240} = 12.5 \text{ amperes.}$$

From Ohm's law:

$$12.5 \text{ amperes} = \frac{\text{Pressure in volts (240).}}{\text{Resistance in ohms}}$$

Therefore:

$$\text{Resistance in ohms} = \frac{240}{12.5} = 19.2 \text{ ohms.}$$

NOTE: These simple but fundamental formulae apply to direct current and ordinary alternating current circuits in which the appliances used—radiators, immersion heaters, filament lamps, and the like—are mainly users of electricity by means of resistance wires that grow hot when current flows.   When appliances that use motors and such devices as the electro-magnetic choke coils in fluorescent lamps are considered, the formulae have to be modified to take into account the electro-magnetic effects of the current: but the modifications needed for domestic and similar installations are usually so small that they can be ignored.   They only become significant where larger industrial installations are concerned.

The unit of electricity

Although not strictly a matter concerning the electrical installation itself, it is as well to complete the picture by mention-ing the current usage of various appliances.

An appliance—say, a one-bar electric fire—is designed so that when it is connected to the usual 240-volt mains, it will use 1000 watts, that is, 1 kilowatt.

If such a 1-kilowatt fire is switched on for exactly 1 hour, it will draw 1 kilowatt-hour of current from the mains.

One kilowatt-hour, or Board of Trade Unit, is the legal unit of electricity consumption.

You can use one unit of electricity by:

burning a 1-kilowatt fire for 1 hour,
burning a $\frac{1}{2}$-kilowatt fire for 2 hours,
burning a 2-kilowatt fire for $\frac{1}{2}$ hour.

To take another example, a 25-watt lamp used for 1 hour:

25 watts $\times$ 1 hour $=$ 25 watt-hours $=$

$\frac{1}{40}$th of 1000 watt-hours $= \frac{1}{40}$th of a unit

or,

25 watts for 40 hours $=$ 25 $\times$ 40 watt-hours $=$

1000 watt-hours $=$ 1 unit.

One further example: a cooker hotplate has a capacity, or loading, of 4 kilowatts.

4 kilowatts ($=$ 4000 watts) for 1 hour $=$

4 kilowatt-hours $=$ 4 units.

2

MATERIALS FOR WIRING INSTALLATIONS

Wiring: general

Wiring may be carried out in several ways, which are conveniently discussed under four headings:

the conductor,
the insulation,
the sheath,
the enclosure.

THE CONDUCTOR

In the majority of cases the conductors used in domestic or small commercial wiring installations are made of high conductivity copper, sometimes covered with a coating of tin to assist in preventing corrosion. In some cases, however, aluminium conductors are used.

To give maximum flexibility, a number of small wires are stranded (twisted) together to make a larger conductor, although sometimes a single strand wire is used.

The important aspect of the conductor is of course the total cross-sectional area of the metal, since the larger the metal area, the greater the current-carrying capacity (subject to certain other factors).

The area is given by stating the number of strands and their diameter. For example, a wire size very commonly used is known as 2·5 mm². This means that the conductor has a cross-sectional area of 2·5 mm².

THE INSULATION

To insulate the live conductors, various methods are used.

Rubber

This is the oldest form of insulation, and is still used, but is largely superseded by plastic materials for all but special applications. A special form of rubber known as butyl rubber is commonly used.

The tough rubber is extruded on to the conductor, to a thickness in a typical case, of a 2·5 mm² conductor for 600/1000 volt working (i.e. for single-phase or 3-phase circuits up to those voltage limits) of 1·14 mm.

Rubber is very flexible, but has a number of disadvantages. It burns easily, and it can be attacked by chemicals and by oil. It is to some extent absorbent to water. Direct sunlight soon causes rubber to deteriorate, so unprotected rubber cables should never be used outdoors. It is also attacked by certain insects, and in any case it ages and tends to become brittle.

A type of rubber-insulated conductor that has been very widely employed is known as v.r.i. (vulcanised rubber insulated). It is made up of an inner insulation of rubber and an outer coating of vulcanised rubber, covered with a coloured fabric braiding. These conductors, used as single cores, have in the past been widely employed for drawing into steel piping (conduit: see Enclosures) that protects them against mechanical damage.

Plastic insulation

There are several forms of plastic materials that are commonly used to insulate wiring conductors. First there is polyvinyl chloride (P.V.C.) which is extremely tough, will not support combustion, and is not affected by water, oil, or most chemicals. It has however a definite temperature limit, above which it will melt and leave the conductor bare.

Then there is polythene insulation, made from a different type of plastic, with a lower safe temperature rating.

Mineral insulation

Under the heading ' sheaths ', mention will be made of mineral-insulated cables, now very widely used especially for such purposes as buried cable runs, cable connections to hot fixed appliances such as boilers, and the like.

This type of wiring system is especially recommended for surface wiring on old buildings.

THE SHEATH

The insulated conductor is more often than not grouped with others within an insulated sheath, to form a *cable*. A cable may have two or more *cores*—each core being a separately insulated conductor, except where the earth connection is also carried within the sheath. A common form of cable consists of two cores and earth—a red-coloured insulated conductor for connection to the live, or phase wire, and a black-coloured insulated conductor for connection to the neutral wire, together with an uninsulated (bare) earth continuity conductor (Fig. 2.1).

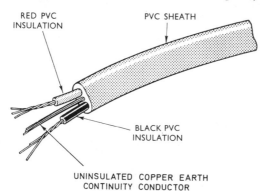

Fig. 2.1. The earth continuity conductor commonly incorporated in sheathed cable.

These three cores are usually laid in a flat formation surrounded by a sheath or outer casing, for protection.

The cable may be made up with a single core, which still has an outer sheath for protection against mechanical damage, or with any number of cores. For 3-phase circuits there will be three phase conductors, each coloured brown, and a neutral conductor, coloured blue, all within the sheath.

Sheaths may be made up as follows:

Tough rubber

These cables are known as t.r.s. (tough rubber sheathed). Rubber sheathing is usually employed with rubber-insulated cores.

Lead sheathing

Rubber-insulated cores are sometimes sheathed in lead alloy. This system affords a considerable degree of protection to the cores against corrosion, although not against mechanical damage. It does however involve special care in ensuring that the lead sheath is made to be continuous throughout the circuit, and this in turn means that the proper fittings for this system, adapted to take the lead sheath, must always be used.

Plastic sheathing

For P.V.C.-insulated cores a P.V.C. sheath is most often used. A variant is a polythene-insulated core or cores covered with a P.V.C. sheath.

Mineral-insulated sheaths

These cables, though more expensive than the flexible sheathed type mentioned above, are capable of being used in situations where no other cable could be employed.

Single-strand copper wires are embedded in a tightly compressed white powder insulation within a copper or aluminium sheath. The powder is made of magnesium oxide (see Fig. 2.2).

The M.I. cable can be subjected to the full heat of a blowlamp without damage, and since the copper sheath will protect the cores against corrosion, the cables may be buried in the ground

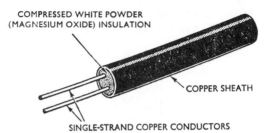

COMPRESSED WHITE POWDER
(MAGNESIUM OXIDE) INSULATION

COPPER SHEATH

SINGLE-STRAND COPPER CONDUCTORS

FIG. 2.2. Mineral-insulated copper-sheathed cable.

except where the soil is acid. The cable may be supplied with an outer coating of plastic or bitumen that enables even the hazard of acid ground to be overcome.

The only disadvantage (apart from cost) of the M.I. cable is that great care must be taken when it is cut and made off into a terminal. This is because the magnesium oxide is hygroscopic —in effect, it attracts moisture, which can reduce the insulation value. Therefore the ends of any M.I. cable must at all times be kept properly sealed, using the special sealing equipment supplied by the manufacturers. When the cable is cut and made off, the simple instructions supplied by the makers must always be carefully followed.

THE ENCLOSURE

According to the best practice, all electric wiring is completely protected against mechanical damage by being inserted in a suitable form of enclosure.

Solid-drawn galvanised steel screwed conduit

The best (but most expensive) system is the solid-drawn galvanised steel screwed conduit, or pipe.

In this system, a complete enclosure made of screwed piping, and including all termination boxes and joint boxes, is provided. The steel conduit is cut to length, bent if necessary, and screwed so that it provides a perfect seal where it enters a termination box or where it is jointed (see Fig. 2.3).

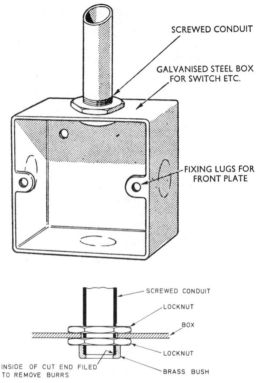

FIG. 2.3.   Typical box for the mounting of the switch or other fitment, on a conduit system.

The conduit system means the use of a considerable number of special tools such as dies, bending machines, pipe vices, and saws. It is costly, as mentioned above, and although it should always be designed in accordance with the Regulations so that the conduits are not tightly packed with wire, and draw-in points should always be accessible, it is nevertheless not always easy to alter or extend a conduit system. A certain degree of skill and experience is needed before a conduit system is embarked upon, although there are no insuperable difficulties that could not be overcome by anyone used to handling metal-working tools.

Welded black-enamelled conduit

Cheaper than the solid-drawn galvanised type, the welded black-enamelled steel conduit, which is also screwed at every joint, is perfectly suitable for domestic premises and situations where corrosive fumes or excessive temperatures are not encountered.

There is also a type of conduit known as ' Silver Grey ', with a finish of this colour, which is widely used where the conduit has to be painted after installation.

Other types of conduit

Aluminium alloy conduits are sometimes used, and these must be screwed at joints and installed in the same way as steel conduits. They are subject to corrosion when embedded in cement and plaster, but may be protected by bitumastic paint.

Non-metallic conduit systems are nowadays widely employed. These are made from a form of plastic substance which can be bent to enable it to be inserted round corners. Some systems use screwed ends to fit into joints and terminal boxes, other systems employ cemented joints. This system is particularly suitable for installation where there is a strong possibility of corrosion, but where mechanical damage is not likely.

Protective channelling

While the conduit systems mentioned previously are used for the highest class of work and enclose single-core P.V.C. cables to the required number, many domestic installations employ P.V.C. sheathed cable, run on the surface where it is safe from damage, but protected when immersed in plaster by means of shaped metal channelling, or by short lengths of round or oval plastic tubing (Fig. 2.4).

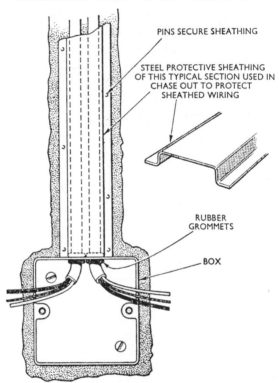

FIG. 2.4.   Installing sheathed cable beneath plaster,
showing protective metal channelling.

Steel and plastic trunking

Where a large number of cables have to be run in one direction, steel or plastic trunking, often of square section with a screwed-down or clipped removable lid is used (Fig. 2.5). The trunking must be electrically continuous and bonded securely to earth, if steel. Plastic trunking must have an insulated earth wire, coloured green, run between all apparatus connected to the system.

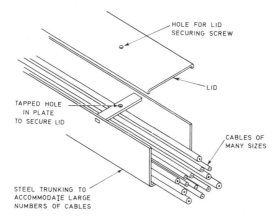

FIG. 2.5. Where a number of cables follow the same route, steel or plastic trunking may be used to protect them, but the number of cables in each run is limited by the Wiring Regulations.

Though more expensive to install than conduit, trunking will often prove to be a good investment.

Suppose, for instance, a small business was started in a workshop, where initially only a few lights and one or two machines were required. This installation could be completed using P.V.C. cables in conduit, at moderate cost. If trunking was used, run at a high level on the walls around the room then the positions of lights, switches and machines could be fed using conduits, connected to the trunking and run down the walls to each position.

Though much of the trunking run would be superfluous at first, there would be plenty of room in the trunking for future additional wiring in the case of business expansion, requiring extra lights and machines, sockets, etc.

3

THE ELECTRICAL LAYOUT

As mentioned earlier, all electrical systems depend on there being a complete circuit from the sources of supply to the appliance, such as a lamp, that is to be fed with current.

In an installation supplied in the ordinary way from the Electricity Board's mains, the source of supply is the supply terminals on the consumer's fuseboard.

Assuming a single-phase supply (and even if a 3-phase supply cable is brought into the house, it is equivalent to three separate single-phase supplies) the live terminals are the consumer's side of the phase fuse and the neutral terminal.

But we have seen that there still exist non-standard supplies in small areas of Britain, and of course supplies in other countries may not be made in accordance with British conventions.

In these cases, the two conductors may both be live to earth, at half the supply voltage (the 3-wire system), or in some rare cases neither conductor may be earthed at the supply end.

In general, however, what has been mentioned above applies very widely.

Every circuit must start from the phase fuse terminal and return to the neutral terminal.

Circuits are interrupted so that the power may be controlled by:

> switches,
> fuses,
> contactors and relays,
> time switches,
> thermostats.

SWITCHES

The simplest circuit consists of a pair of wires from the mains terminals supplying one appliance, say a lamp.

In this circuit there must be a switch, and that switch (if single pole) must be situated in the live phase wire, and *not* in the neutral wire (see Fig. 3.1).

This requirement, which is of course part of the Wiring Regulations, is especially important. If an appliance, for example, a vacuum cleaner, is connected to a switched socket-outlet, and the plug is left inserted, the appliance may not be in operation because the switch is off, and therefore any uninstructed person, or perhaps a child, might start to tinker with it, thinking that because it is not running, it is dead. But if the switch was placed so that it interrupted the neutral (black) wire and not the live (red) wire, the live phase of the supply would be carried through the flexible cable to the appliance, even if it is not running, and a fatal shock might result from anyone interfering with the appliance.

The next variant of the simple one-lamp circuit is the two-way switch (Fig. 3.2), used for example on staircases so that a person can switch off the downstairs light after he has gone upstairs, or vice versa.

In this circuit, the switches can have two positions, either of which can light the lamp. Suppose switch A is in the upper position, and switch B is in the lower position, as in the upper diagram in the figure. There is no circuit, so the lamp is out.

Now imagine a person near switch B turns the switch to the upper position. A circuit is established, and the lamp lights. He ascends the stairs and reaches switch A, and desires to turn the lamp out. He brings switch A to the lower position, and the lamp is extinguished. A second person, at switch B, has only to move his switch to the lower position for the lamp to light once more.

Many switches, notably those of the rocker type (i.e. with a rocking bar in place of the simple knob protruding from a hole

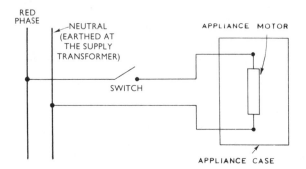

WHEN PROPERLY CONNECTED AS ABOVE, OPENING THE
SWITCH REMOVES ALL POSSIBILITY OF SHOCK

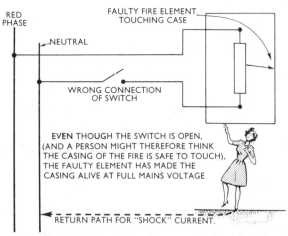

FIG. 3.1. The switch must always be installed in the
phase or live wire, and not in the neutral. The lower
diagram shows what happens if the switch is wrongly
installed and an appliance becomes faulty.

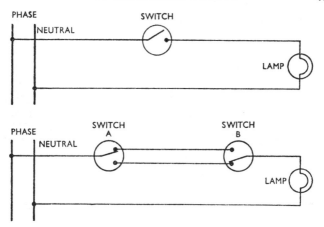

NOTE: THESE AND OTHER SWITCHES ARE NORMALLY INDICATED ON DIAGRAMS LIKE THIS:—

FIG. 3.2. The principle of the two-way switch.

in the cover), are often made only as two-way switches. But if switches of the older type are purchased, obviously care must be taken when necessary to see that the two-way design is bought. It should always be realised that any two-way switch can be used as a single-way switch, if needed.

Suppose now that on a long staircase, for example, with several landings, it is desired to arrange for the light to be switched on and off at several points. In this case intermediate switches are used.

The two wires between the switches *A* and *B* in the figure are called the strapping wires. If, in the case shown in the top diagram, the wires were to be reversed, a circuit would be established and the lamp would light.

The intermediate switch carries out this reversal of the

strapping wires, and any number of intermediate switches may be installed (see Fig. 3.3).

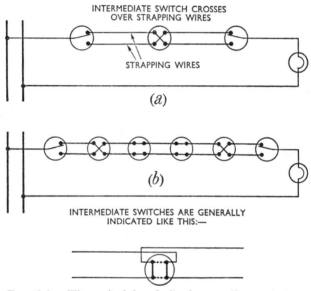

FIG. 3.3.   The principle of the intermediate switch to control a lamp or other loads from a number of positions.

In the figure the upper diagram shows a single intermediate switch and in the lower diagram there are four such switches. The two positions of the switch contacts can be seen from the two diagrams.   In the circuit shown in the lower diagram, the lamp can be turned off and on from six positions.

FUSES

Fuses are found on domestic installations at three points.

It should be made clear that with normal, standard supplies only one phase wire is fused. The neutral connection simply has a link. It is totally incorrect, and in contravention of the

I.E.E. Regulations, to fuse the neutral side, but there are exceptions to this rule, as we shall see later.

First, there are the Electricity Board's main fuses, or cut-outs as they are called (see Fig. 3.4). These are sealed, and must not

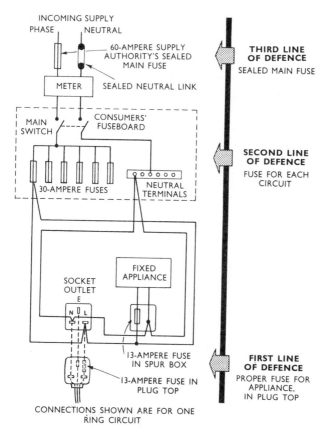

FIG. 3.4. Fused protection on a domestic installation showing the three lines of defence against the consequences of faulty apparatus.

be interfered with. If the main fuse blows, the Electricity
Board's engineers must be called out to replace it.

Secondly, there is the consumer's fuseboard, with a fuse for
each circuit or group of circuits, and a main switch for that
fuseboard. (NOTE: this is the only switch nowadays provided.
The Electricity Board no longer provides a main switch for the
whole installation. To switch everything off, it is necessary to
switch off the main switches on each fuseboard, if there is more
than one. But it should not be forgotten that inside each fuseboard the wires from the Board's meter are still alive.)

The fuses used on the consumer's fuseboard may be of one
of two types: rewireable fuses, or cartridge fuses (Fig. 1.6).

Rewireable fuses

Rewireable fuses are perhaps the most widely used, A fuse
bridge, or fuseholder, of non-inflammable material, is equipped
with screws for holding a suitable length of fuse wire. This wire
is usually threaded through an asbestos tube, or otherwise held
in some way that will ensure that if the wire gets hot and ultimately melts or fuses, no fire damage can result.

The rewireable fuse is convenient in the sense that if a reel of
fuse wire is handy a blown fuse can be rapidly replaced at any
time, that is, if the faulty appliance or section of wiring has been
repaired or isolated from the mains.

Perhaps the rewireable fuse may sometimes be considered as
too convenient, because it is too easy for unwise people to
replace a blown fuse wire with a wire of the wrong size.

If a 30-ampere circuit is properly fused, the fuse will blow if
the current much exceeds 30 amperes for any length of time, and
if all parts of the circuit are properly proportioned, no harm will
result. But if the fuseholder is renewed with thicker fuse wire,
which will allow, say, a 50-ampere current to flow continuouslv,
some part of the circuit—perhaps a switch, or a flexible cable, or
a socket-outlet—may become overheated and a fire could possibly
result.

When replacing a fuse wire, always make sure that the screws
are properly tight, but not too tight to nip the wire and reduce

its current-carrying capacity. Check that the wire is properly fitted into the safety tube or path through the fuseholder. Do not strain the wire too tightly between the terminals, as tightening up may stretch it and reduce the copper section.

Fuseholders are usually marked with the *maximum* size of fuse wire they should carry. This figure should never be exceeded.

Cartridge fuses

The best type of fuse is one in which the actual fusible element is enclosed in a flame-proof cartridge. In some cases the cartridge is filled with a type of sand intended to extinguish any flame that might result from a fuse blowing as a result of a heavy excess of current.

The cartridge fuse is made in various sizes, such as 5, 10, 15, 20, 30, 60 ampere and so on. The fuseholder will only take the appropriate size of cartridge, so that there should never be any danger of inserting the wrong fuse.

On the other hand, the cartridge fuse is slightly more expensive than the rewireable type, and there is always the problem of being caught with no spare cartridge of the correct size. It is unwise to try and repair a blown cartridge fuse.

The best consumer's intake point fuseboard installation will consist of a cartridge equipment, each circuit being properly labelled as to its destination and the size of fuse needed, with an adequate supply of cartridge fuses in a convenient spot nearby.

The third place in the household wiring system where a fuse may be found is in the plug top in the 13-ampere plug (Fig. 3.5).

This plug, now the recognised standard (British Standard 1363) has three ' square ' pins (rectangular, to be precise) and the live side is connected through a fuse. The fuses available are: 2 ampere, black; 3 ampere, red; 5 ampere, black; 10 ampere, black; 13 ampere, brown.

Care should always be taken to ensure that the correct size of fuse is inserted in the plug to suit the appliance to which it is connected.

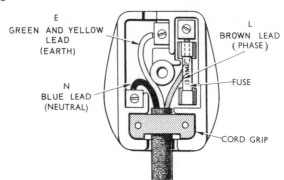

FIG. 3.5. The fused plug top and the method
of connection.

Miniature circuit-breakers

There is an alternative to the intake fuseboard. Small automatic circuit-breakers are now available, fitting into much the
same size as the equivalent fuse (see Fig. 3.6).

A circuit-breaker is an automatic switch. It is so arranged that
if a current of greater value than that for which it is set should
pass through the device, the switch will open automatically and
cut off the circuit, so preventing damage in the same way as a
fuse.

The automatic operation of a circuit-breaker is known as
'tripping'—the switch trips a catch that holds it in.

Trip mechanisms take two forms, both of which may be used
on the same switch.

An electromagnet—a coil of wire wound on an iron frame—
has a mechanical pull that corresponds to the current passing
through its coil. The current through the switch is taken through
such a coil, arranged with an arm, attracted by the magnet, that
can flick the switch to the off position if the current is too
great.

In the second type of trip mechanism, a bimetal strip is used.
All metals expand when heated, some more than others. If two

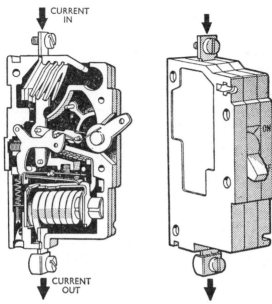

CURRENT
IN

CURRENT
OUT

FIG. 3.6. The miniature circuit-breaker, sometimes used in preference to a fuse (reproduction of a Crabtree design).

strips of metal, one with a high rate of expansion with heat, and the other with a low rate, are joined only at their ends, when heat is applied the combined strip will bow, or bend, as the different rates of expansion come into play. Inside the switch there is a very small heater element that carries the main current. If the current is excessive, this element gets hot and causes the nearby bimetal strip to bend, and a linkage then trips the switch.

With the electromagnetic type of trip, the switch can be closed again immediately it has tripped. (It may trip again if the cause is still there.) But with the thermal, or bimetal-strip type, the switch cannot be closed again for a minute or two, as the heater element and the bimetal strip have first to cool down.

TIME SWITCHES

A time switch is often used for controlling such circuits as shop-window lighting, central heating and the like. Like all other switches, the actual contacts of the time switch must be wired into the live side of the circuit, and not into the neutral, and care must be taken that the rating of the time-switch contacts—for example, 10 amperes, as indicated on the nameplate—is not exceeded by the appliances on its circuit.

Time switches may be of several kinds. In some, known as the spring-rewind type, an electric motor winds a clockwork system, so that if the supply should fail, the clock will continue to run, and will open and close the contacts at the proper time, for a period which may be a few hours or a few days. In other designs, the clock is electrically operated, and will stop if the mains supply fails, and set to the correct time when the supply is resumed.

In both cases, there must be a separate, fuse-protected circuit to the clock motor. Some clocks have the motor-circuit fuse incorporated in the case. In other instances, it is necessary to provide a 2-ampere fuse and a separate connection.

THERMOSTATS

Thermostats are temperature-operated devices, which are arranged to open or close a circuit as the temperature rises or falls. For room heating control, they may work in the range of 20° C to 10° C, while for refrigerator applications they may operate in the range of 0° C to −10° C.

In many cases, bimetal strips, mentioned earlier, are used. As the temperature rises, for example the bimetal strip heats and bends so that ultimately the contact is broken and the heater circuit switched off. To prevent the contacts ' dithering ' and consequently arcing, the contact piece is usually equipped with a small magnet, and as the bimetal strip slowly bends it is suddenly snapped to the open or closed position, as the case may be, thus giving a clean break (see Fig. 3.7).

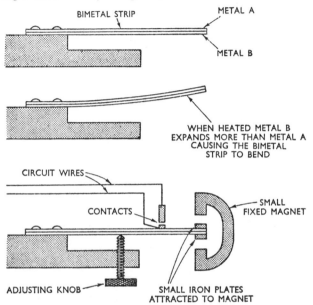

FIG. 3.7. The principle of the thermostat. A refrigerator thermostat is shown, switching on the unit as the temperature increases.

Thermostats should always be wired into the live side of the circuit, and again the current rating of the contacts should never be exceeded.

RELAYS AND CONTACTORS

Devices such as time switches and thermostats have switching contacts that are limited in their capacity, usually to circuits of about 3 kilowatts. If the time switch, for example, is to be used for larger circuits, some auxiliary device is necessary. Small devices of this kind are called relays, larger examples are known as contactors.

An electromagnetic coil is supplied with current by the closing of the time-switch contact, and when this coil is energised it attracts an armature that in turn closes much larger contacts than those with which a time switch could be fitted: in fact, a contactor could control a load of 100 kilowatts or more (see Fig. 3.8).

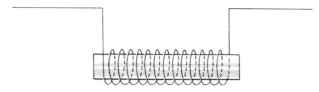

PRINCIPLE OF THE ELECTRO MAGNET. WHEN CURRENT PASSES THROUGH THE COIL WOUND ROUND THE IRON CORE THE IRON BECOMES MAGNETISED

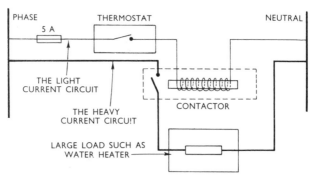

SCHEMATIC DIAGRAM OF A CONTACTOR IN A TYPICAL CIRCUIT. THE SMALL CONTACTS ON THE THERMOSTAT CAN CONTROL A FINAL CIRCUIT OF ANY SIZE

FIG. 3.8. The principle of the contactor.

A relay is a smaller version of the contactor, and is usually of the type where the originating current is very small, such as the output from electronic devices like 'electric eye' cells or amplifiers. Daylight-operated street lighting circuits provide an example of a circuit where relays are used.

In connecting up contactors and relays, care must be taken to fuse the control circuit with a light fuse (a 5-ampere fuse is usually sufficient) and then to see that the fusing on the main circuit is adequate.

Both the control circuit and the main circuit must be wired into the live side, as for all switches or circuit-breaking devices.

THE CIRCUIT LAYOUT

We can now consider the circuit layout for a typical installation, for example, a four-bedroomed house.

Bearing in mind the first principle that each circuit must have proper protection by being adequately fused, one's mind must first turn to a system whereby every light, every appliance (such as a fixed radiator or cooker or refrigerator) and every socket-outlet had its own separate cable back to the main consumer's fuseboard, and was individually connected to a separate fuse of the appropriate size.

This would indeed be the perfect and ideal system (see Fig. 3.9), but would be extremely expensive on account of the lengths of cable needed and the number of fuses required. It is also unnecessary.

To consider the extreme alternative, suppose an installation had only one main fuse, to which all the circuits were connected. If this fuse blew, through a fault of any one appliance, such as a desk lamp, the whole house would be plunged in darkness. In any case, proper *graded* protection for the various circuits could not be provided in this way.

The practical solution obviously lies somewhere between these two extremes.

The I.E.E. Wiring Regulations state that the number of circuits that may be grouped together on one fuse relates to the total demand on the circuit, evolved according to certain rules. For example, consider a lighting circuit. This might well originate at a 15-ampere fuse at the main consumer's fuseboard. It is

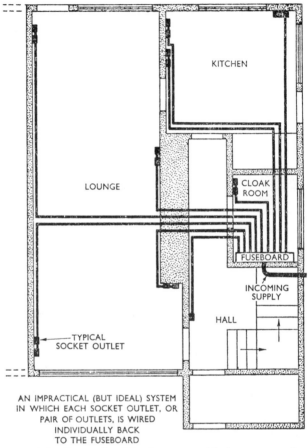

KITCHEN

LOUNGE

CLOAK ROOM

FUSEBOARD

INCOMING SUPPLY

HALL

TYPICAL SOCKET OUTLET

AN IMPRACTICAL (BUT IDEAL) SYSTEM IN WHICH EACH SOCKET OUTLET, OR PAIR OF OUTLETS, IS WIRED INDIVIDUALLY BACK TO THE FUSEBOARD

FIG. 3.9. Domestic wiring layout: an ideal system, rarely used.

laid down that each fixed lampholder must be assumed to carry a 100-watt lamp. Now a 100-watt lamp consumes 0·416 ampere. So 35 lampholders could legitimately be supplied from a single

15-ampere lighting circuit—*providing the correct size of cabling was used throughout the circuit.*

But this would not be practicable in the house we are discussing, since the wiring would become somewhat cumbersome and in any case it would be undesirable for every light in the house to go out if a single lampholder developed a fault.

A commonly used system would be to have two 15-ampere lighting circuits, one for the first floor and one for the ground floor, with perhaps ten or so lampholders wired to each. In this way there would be some light left in the house if one lampholder failed, and in addition the circuits would be a little underloaded so that extensions would always be possible.

Turning now to fixed appliances—cookers, water heaters, fixed radiators, and refrigerators—some of these (except perhaps refrigerators) are heavily loaded appliances, often calling for 15 kilowatts or more in the case of cookers, 3 kilowatts for water heaters, and so on.

The I.E.E. Regulations call for a separate sub-circuit for every appliance rated at 15 amperes and above, except in the special circumstances mentioned later when the ring circuit is discussed.

Therefore some of these fixed appliances should in fact have a separate circuit back to its own fuse, of appropriate size, on the main consumer's fuseboard. Even if some appliances, such as a particular fixed radiator, do not initially require more than 2 kilowatts ($8\frac{1}{2}$ amperes) it is strongly recommended that the supply board should be wired back to the main switchboard on the basis of a single feed of 15 amperes' capacity: no one can tell if at some time in the future a larger radiator may not be needed at that point. Experience shows that the usage of electricity steadily grows, not only for installing *more* appliances but in substituting new, more heavily loaded appliances for older ones. For example—to mention a portable appliance—the elements fitted to electric kettles have grown in loading from 600 watts about 10 years ago and have now reached 3000 watts or even more.

The ring circuit

Anyone who thinks carefully about the circuit arrangements

set out above will soon reach the conclusion that there is some inevitable wastage of copper—that is, there is more current-carrying capacity than is needed *for most of the time*.

On the whole, it is better to have a little extra capacity in the circuits, to allow for extension. But there is a very widely used system that allows much fuller use to be made of the current-carrying capacity of the circuits installed.

This system is called the ring circuit (Fig. 3.10), and it is based on the application of what is called the principle of 'diversity'.

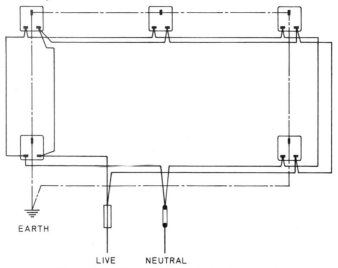

FIG. 3.10. The principle of the ring circuit.

Take any ordinary house, and consider the time and place at which various appliances are used.

The largest portable electricity-consuming appliance commonly used in domestic premises is the 3-kilowatt fire. It is extremely unlikely that more than three such fires will be in use, at full load, at the same time, even in the coldest weather, at any rate on the ground floor.

Therefore, if there are, say, eight socket-outlets on the ground floor, each of 13 amperes capacity (thus capable of taking the 3-kilowatt fire) it would be extremely generous in copper to wire each one separately back to the fuseboard. When the three large fires were in use, the remaining five sockets on the ground floor are likely to be used only for very light current appliances like lamps, radio and television sets.

Now suppose all the 13-ampere standard socket-outlets on the ground floor were connected in a ring. That is, a pair of 2·5 mm² wires starts at one 30-ampere fuse at the main fuseboard and runs to the first socket, on to the second, the third, and so on, and then back to the *same* 30-ampere fuse (see Fig. 3.11).

The ring circuit, now very widely used, is based on the employment of a standard socket-outlet, of 13 amperes' capacity, and having a fuse in the plug top. This socket-outlet will allow for a 3-kilowatt appliance being connected, as such an appliance will need 12·48 amperes.

The ring circuit cannot normally be used with any other type of socket-outlet: only those 13-ampere designs made to British Standard 1363, and used with the appropriate 3-pin fused plugs, may be employed.

In this system, each 13-ampere socket has two connections back to the mains—each capable of carrying 13 amperes at least. The *maximum* use is made of the *minimum* amount of copper in the cables: that is, the minimum length of cabling is employed for a given number of socket-outlets.

The use of the ring circuit, as mentioned above, is only possible because of the diversity of usage that naturally evolves. In an ordinary dining room, where there might be perhaps six 13-ampere standard socket-outlets, it is inconceivable that more than two 3-kilowatt fires would be in use at the same time, even under arctic conditions. Fires, as mentioned earlier, are the largest portable current-consuming appliances likely to be used in domestic premises. Any other appliances use so much less current that they do not need to be taken into account in this connection.

58

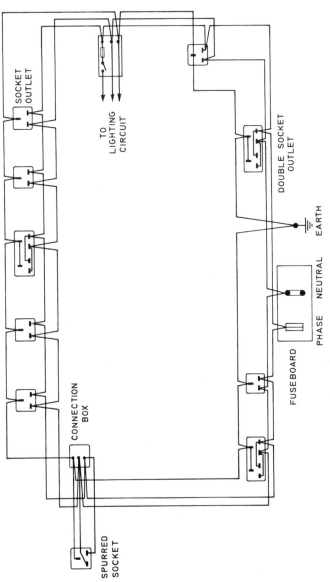

FIG. 3.11. The ring circuit in greater detail.

The Regulations regarding the use of the ring circuit are:

If the floor area concerned does not exceed 100 square metres there can be an unlimited number of 13-ampere standard socket-outlets on the ring, which must consist of 2·5 mm² conductors and must terminate in a 30-ampere fuse.

NOTE: In practice, in domestic premises, the requirement mentioned above usually means that two separate rings are needed. A convenient division is to have a downstairs ring and an upstairs ring (see Fig. 3.13).
The more the rooms embraced by the ring, the greater the diversity. (People do not, in general, use all the rooms in a house at the same time, and even if they did, their current-using habits do not coincide.)

There are several additional features of the ring circuit to be mentioned. In addition to the main 13-ampere socket-outlets, it is possible to install any number of specially designed connections for very small current appliances such as clocks (Fig. 3.12) and shaver supplies, *providing* each connection is made by means of the proper fused connector designed for the purpose, complying with British Standard 3052.

Although the rule still holds good that appliances consuming above 3 kilowatts, such as cookers and large immersion heaters, should be wired back separately and individually to appropriate

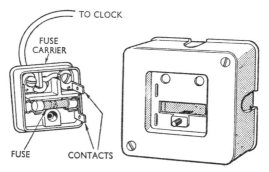

FIG. 3.12. A fused clock connector.

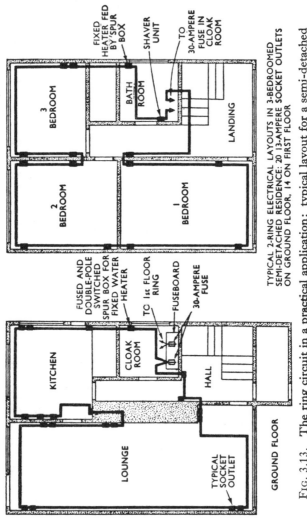

FIXED HEATER FED BY SPUR BOX

SHAVER UNIT

TO 30-AMPERE FUSE IN CLOAK ROOM

3 BEDROOM

BATH ROOM

2 BEDROOM

1 BEDROOM

LANDING

FUSED AND DOUBLE-POLE SWITCHED SPUR BOX FOR FIXED WATER HEATER

TO 1st FLOOR RING

FUSEBOARD

30-AMPERE FUSE

KITCHEN

CLOAK ROOM

HALL

LOUNGE

TYPICAL SOCKET OUTLET

GROUND FLOOR

TYPICAL 2-RING ELECTRICAL LAYOUTS IN 3-BEDROOMED SEMI-DETACHED RESIDENCE: 20 13-AMPERE SOCKET OUTLETS ON GROUND FLOOR, 14 ON FIRST FLOOR

Fig. 3.13. The ring circuit in a practical application: typical layout for a semi-detached house, showing two rings

fuses on the main fuseboard, nevertheless there is a strong tendency, in domestic wiring practice, for more and more fixed appliances (each one not exceeding 3 kilowatts) to be wired into the ring, to secure the maximum economy in the use of cable. Such instances include water heaters other than immersion heaters, small ' table ' cookers, fixed radiators of up to 3 kilowatts, and many other appliances.

It should be noted that special regulations, to be mentioned later, apply to the method of connection of certain fixed appliances to the ring.

Spur connections

It is permissible to connect a spur (or tap-off, or ' tee ' connection) to a ring circuit (see Fig. 3.14), to obviate the need to run two wires to an isolated area, providing the following Regulation is observed:

> When spurs supplying outlying socket-outlets are connected to a ring circuit, not more than two socket-outlets or one fixed appliance shall be fed from each, and the total number of spurs shall not exceed the total number of socket-outlets and stationary appliances connected directly to the ring. Spurs shall be connected to a ring circuit in socket-outlets, or in suitable joint- or junction-boxes.
>
> The conductors supplying the spur shall not be smaller than those forming the ring itself.

There is another variant of the spur connection—the fused spur box (see Fig. 3.15). This device is a connecting box fitted with a cartridge fuse which can be replaced easily, usually from the front of the box. It is useful in cases where an isolated lighting circuit, made up of fixed lampholders, needs to be supplied. The use of the fused spur box, fitted, say, with a 5-ampere fuse, obviates the need for a special wiring run back to the fuseboard to supply one or two lighting points. In this case, the conductors on the spur need only be of a size suitable for the load.

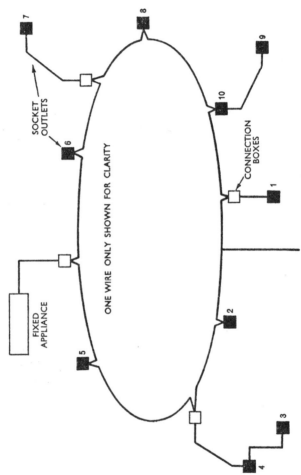

Fig. 3.14. How spur connections may be made, according to the Regulations

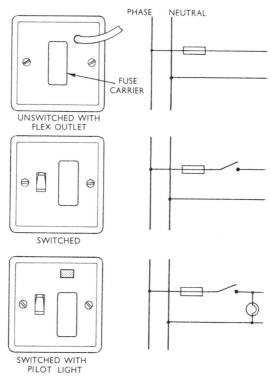

FIG. 3.15. Typical spur boxes, switched and un-
switched, showing the connections.

Radial circuits

Radial circuits are circuits which also utilise 13-ampere flat
pin sockets, to British Standard 1363, except that the circuit is
not wired in the form of a ring. There are three types of radial
circuit, as shown in Fig. 3.16.

The first circuit is a special case, for an installation in a single
room other than a kitchen whose floor area does not exceed
30 m² , then six socket-outlets or fixed appliances may be connected, provided a fixed water heater is not supplied.

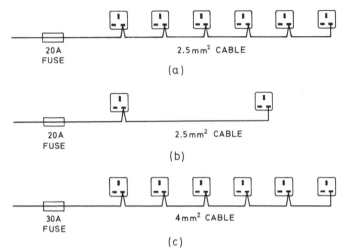

FIG. 3.16. The three types of radial circuits. Live wire only shown
(a) Six sockets or fixed appliances (not a kitchen)
(b) Two sockets or fixed appliances
(c) Six sockets or fixed appliances

The second and third circuits cover any situation other than that previously mentioned, and may supply either two or six socket-outlets or fixed appliances.

Off-peak circuits

In recent years there has been a considerable increase in the number of consumers taking current at cheap rates, during off-peak hours.

In this system, the Area Electricity Board provides a time switch to allow the off-peak supply to be taken at the specified hours only, and a separate meter. Sometimes there may be provided, in addition, a contactor to switch on the off-peak circuits, since the time-switch contacts may not be of large enough current-handling capacity. The consumer himself has to supply the extra fuseboard, allowing for the required number of 30-ampere fuses (often termed ' ways ').

Off-peak supplies are generally used in three ways: for thermal storage heaters, under-floor warming, water heating.

In addition, battery chargers are sometimes fed on the off-peak system.

No other circuits may be connected to the off-peak system.

Each off-peak circuit is wired by an individual cable back to the off-peak fuseboard. The termination points are always in the form of fixed spur units—that is outlet boxes fitted with replaceable cartridge fuses but without socket holes, the connections being permanently made (see Fig. 3.17).

White meter

A common method of offering cheap off-peak rates is by means of a ' White Meter '. With this system the same appliances are used both on and off peak. At the beginning of the off-peak period a sealed time switch energises a relay in the meter which transfers the meter drive from one set of recording dials to another. At the end of the period the time switch de-energises the relay, switching the meter drive back to its original position.

Summary

To sum up, the circuit layout in a typical house comes under the following headings:

Fixed appliances

(*a*) Cookers and immersion heaters, and any other fixed appliances using above 3 kilowatts. (Large current-consuming appliances.)

> *Each appliance wired directly and individually back to the main fuseboard.*

(*b*) Other fixed appliances connected to a ring main.

(*c*) Lighting circuits for fixed lamps. (Light current-consuming appliances.)

> *Grouped in circuits, each circuit wired back to the main fuseboard.*

(*d*) Off-peak circuits, for storage heaters, floor heating, immersion water heaters.

> *Each appliance wired directly and individually back to the main fuseboard.*

66

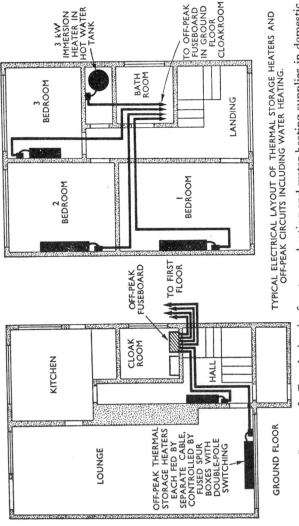

FIG. 3.17. Layout of off-peak circuits for storage heating and water heating supplies in domestic premises

Socket-outlets for portable appliances

In a perfect installation, where cost is no object, each socket-outlet would be wired directly and individually back to the main switchboard.

In practice the ring circuit is used, with spurs as required.

EARTHING

As mentioned earlier, earthing is a means of ensuring electrical safety. All metal parts of all appliances used on the installation should be connected solidly to earth at all times that the appliance is connected to live electric mains.

For fixed appliances, earthing is ensured by a permanent earth connection, which must be solidly connected to an earth point, a feature to be mentioned later. The connection must be made by means of (*a*) the steel conduit, if such a system is properly installed, or (*b*) an earth wire of suitable size. (In general, the earth wire must be at least half the conductor size of the live conductors in the supply cable.)

For portable appliances, fed by means of socket-outlets, the earth connection is ensured by means of the earth pin in the plug. The earth socket, into which this pin enters, must be connected to the earth point by proper permanent means, as in the case of fixed appliances.

In the majority of cases in domestic premises the earth socket is connected to the earth point by means of the uninsulated earth conductor in the sheathed cable itself.

If the existing cable has no earth conductor, the question arises as to how to provide an earth connection, if a new socket-outlet is being installed.

The earth connection

This raises the question as to what is an ' earth ' connection. A wire buried in the earth itself forms a kind of earth connection, but an earth electrode of this kind has to be very carefully designed so that it will not corrode or, for example, find the earth around it becoming so dry that the electrode becomes insulating instead of conducting.

Wherever practicable, the earth electrode is nearly always provided, in effect, by the Area Electricity Board, although this is not obligatory.   In the case of an underground service the incoming supply cable has a lead sheath and steel armouring which is continuous to the carefully designed earth electrode at the substation.   This sheath is usually provided, at the consumer's metering point, with a connection to an earthing terminal.   All the earthing points of the whole installation should be connected back to this earthing terminal, the official earth point (Fig. 3.18).

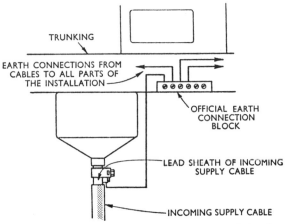

FIG. 3.18. Earthing terminal at the consumer's intake point. Note: this terminal is not always provided by the Area Electricity Board, particularly in rural areas where the supply enters the house from an overhead power line.

But if such a terminal does not exist, what can be done?   In any case, overhead supplies, such as those provided in many rural areas, do not allow for the provision of an 'official' earth point.

The cold water system (*never* the hot water pipes, these may be discontinuous) has often been used as the earth conductor system, however, this is insufficient for the sole means of earthing of an installation, and a separate earth electrode *must* be provided.

The regulations state that gas, water and electricity services must be bonded together for safety (Fig. 3.19). The purpose of bonding the services is to ensure that all metal work within the premises is at the same potential, so reducing the risk of electrical shock.

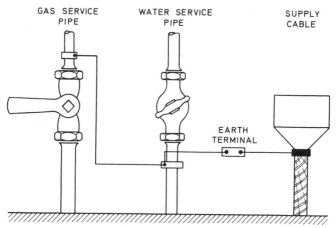

GAS SERVICE PIPE WATER SERVICE PIPE SUPPLY CABLE

EARTH TERMINAL

FIG. 3.19. Bonding of services.

An earth electrode is a metal rod or rods or even plates, set in the ground providing an effectual connection with the general mass of earth. The size of the earth electrode, and of the earthing lead which makes the connection from the electrode to the earthing termination, should be of the correct size, i.e. minimum of 6 mm², maximum 70 mm² depending on the size of the largest conductor within the installation (see Figs. 3.20 and 3.21).

But even with this arrangement, we are not out of all our earthing difficulties where no 'official' earthing point is provided. The ground near the installation may be rocky, or exceptionally dry, or there may be some other condition that leads to a high resistance between the earth electrode and the general mass of earth.

This could give rise to dangerous conditions. The whole ground might become alive, in the neighbourhood of the earth

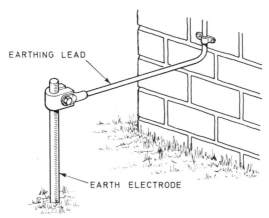

EARTHING LEAD

EARTH ELECTRODE

Fig. 3.20. A typical earth electrode providing an earth point where no other is available.

SAFETY ELECTRICAL EARTH
DO NOT REMOVE

Fig. 3.21. Label to be fitted to earthing lead. Lettering not less than 4·75 mm high.

electrode, at the time of a fault, and a child, for example, touching perhaps a rainwater down-pipe with a water flow into a gutter, could be killed by electrocution, the current passing *from the ground* through his body, to the rainwater pipe (Fig. 3.22).

Earth leakage circuit-breakers

The problem of providing proper earthing facilities under these conditions is solved by the use of the earth leakage circuit-breaker.

Suppose an earth spike, or electrode, is provided. Assume also that it is not very good, in the sense that very dry or rocky ground means that its resistance to the general body of earth is rather high—say up to 100 ohms, instead of much less than 1 ohm, as it should be.

Now imagine a wire connected from the earth point of the wiring installation as a whole to this spike. If then an appliance fails—say an electric iron becomes faulty internally—the live phase wire will become connected to the earth spike, through the green and yellow earthing lead on the iron.

Under ideal conditions this occurrence would immediately cause enough current to flow to blow the fuse, and any danger to the person using the iron would be averted.

But with our high-resistance earth spike, enough current does *not* flow to blow the fuse. The body of the iron remains alive.

However, *some* current does flow, and it is this current that is used to safeguard the installation.

The connection between the earth point of the whole installation and the earth spike is taken through an electromagnetic coil attached to a circuit-breaker, or automatic switch, that is connected in series with the main fuse. Any current flowing through this coil will cause the switch to trip, or open, so disconnecting the mains, and removing all source of danger (see Fig. 3.23).

Earth leakage circuit-breakers can be made to operate on several thousandths of an ampere, so that however high the resistance of the earth spike to the general mass of earth, the circuit-breaker will operate. It should be realised, however, that unlike a fuse it will cut off the whole supply and not only the faulty section.

More than one type of earth leakage circuit-breaker is available. Some—as mentioned above—operate through the passage of the leakage current. That is the type most commonly employed, since it is the cheapest.

It has one or two disadvantages. First, the current path through which the fault current must flow, to earth, may be paralleled somewhere else on the system, as for example in an immersion heater, where the water piping may well provide a second earth path for the fault current, in addition to the path provided by the proper earth continuity connection. This may affect (but not entirely nullify) the sensitivity of the earth leakage circuit-breakers (see Fig. 3.24).

Secondly, it has to be realised that any fault anywhere on the installation will cause the earth leakage circuit-breaker to trip and so cut off the whole installation.   Unlike proper fusing arrangements, there is no selectivity.

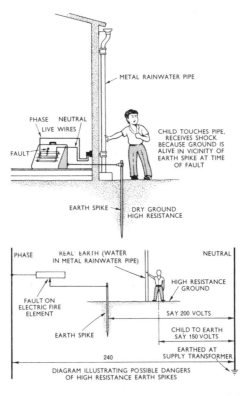

FIG. 3.22. If the earth spike is in dry ground having a high resistance, it is possible that a child or other person touching the metal rainwater pipe through which water is flowing to earth might receive a shock when there is a fault on an electrical appliance, unless measures such as the installation of earth leakage circuit-breakers prevent this danger from arising.

The first of these problems can be solved by the use of the somewhat more expensive current balance earth leakage circuit-breaker.

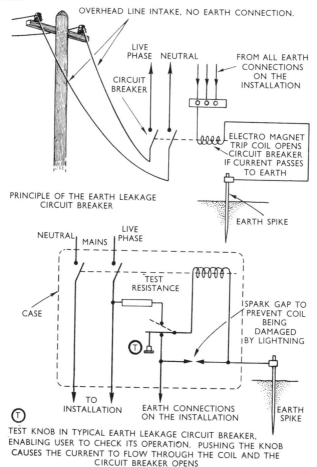

OVERHEAD LINE INTAKE, NO EARTH CONNECTION.

LIVE PHASE   NEUTRAL

FROM ALL EARTH CONNECTIONS ON THE INSTALLATION

CIRCUIT BREAKER

ELECTRO MAGNET TRIP COIL OPENS CIRCUIT BREAKER IF CURRENT PASSES TO EARTH

PRINCIPLE OF THE EARTH LEAKAGE CIRCUIT BREAKER

EARTH SPIKE

NEUTRAL   MAINS   LIVE PHASE

TEST RESISTANCE

CASE

SPARK GAP TO PREVENT COIL BEING DAMAGED BY LIGHTNING

TO INSTALLATION   EARTH CONNECTIONS ON THE INSTALLATION   EARTH SPIKE

TEST KNOB IN TYPICAL EARTH LEAKAGE CIRCUIT BREAKER, ENABLING USER TO CHECK ITS OPERATION. PUSHING THE KNOB CAUSES THE CURRENT TO FLOW THROUGH THE COIL AND THE CIRCUIT BREAKER OPENS

FIG. 3.23. The principle of the earth leakage circuit-breaker.

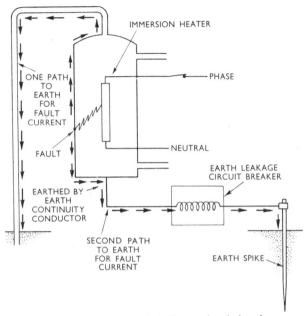

Fig. 3.24. How an earth leakage circuit-breaker may become inoperative if the faulty appliance has a parallel path to earth, for the fault current, for example through water piping.

The current in the phase wire, in any normal circuit, must at all times exactly equal the return current in the neutral wire. If some current is passing from the phase wire to earth, these two currents no longer balance.

The current balance e.l.c.b. uses this condition, by employing in effect two coils, one carrying the phase current and the other the neutral, and so arranging the mechanical parts that if the force exerted by these two coils becomes unequal, the circuit-breaker will trip.

The second problem, the lack of selectivity, can only be solved by splitting the installation up into sections that are entirely separate electrically, each being fitted with a separate earth leakage circuit-breaker, whatever type may be used. The circuit-breakers all have a common earthing point, but on the installation side the earth continuity wires must be kept completely separate from each other (Fig. 3.25). If this separation is carried out, the occurrence of a fault will result in only one circuit-breaker tripping, leaving the remainder of the installation in service.

All earth leakage circuit-breakers are provided with a test knob, so that the user can make sure that his essential protection against shock is in working order. Even the best earth leakage

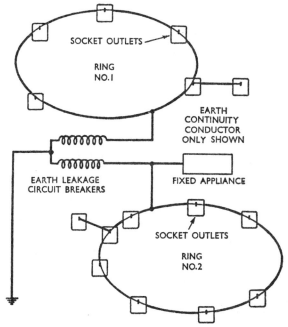

FIG. 3.25. Separation of circuits, where earth leakage circuit-breakers are employed, to allow for selective operation, so that only one portion of the installation is cut off should a fault develop on any part of the wiring or the appliances.

circuit-breakers, after some years of installation without faults occurring, may tend to stick, if not regularly tested.

This matter of earth leakage protection should be discussed with the Electricity Board in each individual case. Their engineers will probably have carried out extensive earth resistance tests in the area concerned, and will be able to advise on the most suitable kind of earth leakage circuit-breaker to install.

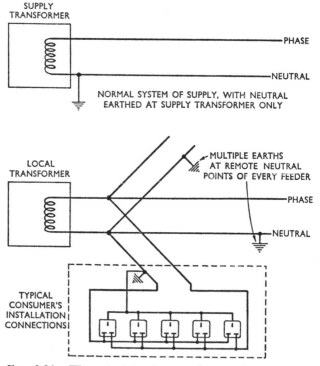

FIG. 3.26. The principle of protective multiple earthing, which can only be used in areas where approval of the Supply Authority and of the appropriate Minister has been obtained.

Protective multiple earthing (p.m.e.)

Another solution to the problem of satisfactory and safe earthing where difficulties are encountered is p.m.e. (protective multiple earthing) (Fig. 3.26), but this is not a system that can be used by the electrician himself.

As we have seen earlier, the normal system of supply has the neutral conductor earthed at the supply transformer only. Normally, this neutral conductor must not be earthed anywhere else, because this could cause stray currents to flow in such other services as telephone cables.

However, sanction from the appropriate Ministry is required before one can apply p.m.e. in a particular area. In this case, the neutral conductor is earthed (by the Electricity Board) at every ' end point ' of every feeder supplied by a particular transformer.

When this p.m.e. system is applied, the neutral conductor on each installation becomes the earth point, and all the earth continuity connections are joined to the neutral, at the supply intake position.

The electrician should consult the Electricity Board about earth connection made in an area in which p.m.e. is being employed. He can learn about this likelihood by consulting the Electricity Board before any installation work commences.

4

PHYSICAL PLAN OF THE INSTALLATION

HAVING decided on the circuit layout, the next problem relates to the physical installation of the wiring.

The first point to decide is the size and type of the cabling.

SIZE OF CABLE

The size of cable to be used is determined by several factors.

1. For a single fixed appliance.

Lighting circuits. Each lampholder or fluorescent lighting fitting must be taken as consuming 100 watts. So if there are six lighting points on a circuit, the current that must be allowed for is 600 watts. This is equivalent to 2·5 amperes, at 240 volts.

The smallest size of cable normally used is 1·0 mm² (one square millimetre in cross-sectional area). This size will carry 11-amperes when used with p.v.c. (polyvinyl chloride compound) insulation and run in conduit with one other wire, or in the form of twin sheathed p.v.c. cable.

Thus the 1·0 mm² size is applicable for circuits with up to 26 lighting points installed.

Permanently connected appliances such as cookers, water heaters, radiators and the like.

For appliances that consume a considerable amount of current, for example a cooker, the total wattage of the appliance must first be ascertained—that is, the loading with all parts switched on to their highest loadings.

Suppose this comes to 6 kilowatts. The current necessary is therefore 25 amperes.

According to the wire tables published in the I.E.E. Wiring Regulations, where conduit is employed or where twin sheathed cable is used, the 6 mm² conductor size will carry 31 amperes, and may thus be used.

But when considering appliances like cookers, it should always be realised that loadings continually increase, and when a new cooker is installed it may be very costly and inconvenient to have to rewire the circuit. Therefore it pays to allow for a larger loading than is strictly necessary. A cable size larger, in the example mentioned above, that is 10 mm² against 6 mm², will allow for 42 amperes, which provides for a loading of just over 10 kilowatts.

However, recent investigations into the usage of cookers and other heavy-current appliances have shown that in normal domestic use the diversity factors that may be applied are considerably greater than had previously been thought. For example, it has been officially stated that a cooker whose total loading, with all plates and oven elements switched on full, is 13 kilowatts, needing about 54 amperes, may in fact be connected by means of a 6 mm² cable, whose nominal rating is 31 amperes.

It must be remembered that if the cable size is increased beyond that strictly necessary, as suggested above in certain cases, the fuse ways must be proportioned to suit the capacity of the cable. But the operation of diversity of demand is such that even the largest cooker used in domestic premises may be supplied from a 30-ampere fuse, that allows for over 7 kilowatts of load. (See Chapter 5, size of fuseboard.)

Ring main

The ring main is permitted, under the Regulations, only for use with 13-ampere socket-outlets fitted with fused plugs. The number of socket-outlets that may be connected has been set out earlier, in Chapter 3. The cable size must not be less than 2·5 mm².

Mineral-insulated cables

Mineral-insulated copper-sheathed cables employ single wires, not stranded conductors, and since the current-carrying capacity of any conductor is related to the heating effect caused by the passage of the current, and the mineral insulation differs from the V.R.I. or p.v.c. type of insulation in regard to its ability to dissipate heat, different cable size rules apply. Table 1 shows the ratings of the sizes most commonly used.

Flexible cords

Flexible cords should always be used to the smallest possible degree, and should be kept as short as possible. They should never be used for permanent wiring.

Four types of flexible cord are commonly used:

for light-current work,
for heavy-current work,
for portable tools, etc.,
for the connection of hot appliances.

For light-current work such as suspending lamps and connecting up lighting fittings, radio sets and the like, where the current does not exceed 3 amperes, the type of flexible cord generally used is twin, plastic-insulated cord, with 0·5 mm² conductors.

For heavy-current appliances such as radiators and the like, three-core plastic-insulated cord, sheathed or covered with braiding, is used, with 1·5 mm² conductors.

For portable tools, a tough rubber-sheathed three-core cable, or an equivalent plastic-insulated cable, with 1·5 mm² conductors, is suitable.

For connections to such appliances as irons, water heaters and any other appliance like a fire or lighting fitting that can become hot, an asbestos-braided cable, of three-core construction, with special heat-resisting plastic, and conductors of 1·5 mm² size, is used.

Wire tables

Table 2 shows the current-carrying capacities and weight-supporting loadings applicable to commonly used flexible cables relating to domestic and small industrial installations.

Table 1. Current rating of mineral-insulated cables

Nominal cross-sectional area of conductor (mm²)	Single-core cables (amperes)	Twin cables (amperes)
1·0	23	19
1·5	29	24
2·5	39	32
4·0	50	41

Abridged from I.E.E. Wiring Regulations, Table 14M, 14th edition.

Table 2. Flexible cords

Size (mm²)	Current ratings (amperes)	Maximum permissible weight that a twin cable should support (kg)
0·5	3	2
0·75	6	3
1·0	10	5
1·5	15	5

Abridged from I.E.E. Wiring Regulations, Table 22M, 14th edition.

Table 3.   Current rating of single-core P.V.C.
insulated cables bunched and enclosed in conduit

Size of cable (mm²)	Two cables (amperes)	Three or four cables (amperes)
1·0	11	9
1·5	13	11
2·5	18	16
4	24	22
6	31	28
10	42	39
16	56	50

Abridged from I.E.E. Wiring Regulations, Table 1M,
14th edition.

Table 4.   Current rating of twin and
multi-core sheathed P.V.C. insulated
cables

Size of cable (mm²)	One twin cored cable (amperes)
1·0	12
1·5	15
2·5	21
4	27
6	35
10	48

Abridged from I.E.E. Wiring Regulations, Table 3M, 14th edition.

NOTE: In using these tables, it is important to note that they
are intended for approximate guidance only, and the full text of
the *I.E.E. Wiring Regulations* should be consulted before they

are applied to anything but the simplest domestic installation. There are important qualifications in the Regulations that must be observed in certain cases; for example the cables must be derated (allotted a lower current-carrying capacity) if the ambient air temperature is high (for example, in the tropics, or in a bakehouse).

TYPE OF CABLING

The conduit system

As mentioned earlier, the best system of all (and the most expensive) is screwed seamless galvanised conduit, enclosing P.V.C.-insulated wire.

If this system is adopted, the system must be electrically continuous throughout: that means that all sections of conduit (piping) must be screwed together, with screwed sleeves to join each section of straight pipe, and properly screwed and terminated lengths running into metal junction boxes and the boxes that receive switches, ceiling roses, fuseboards, socket-outlets, spur boxes, clock connector boxes and all other fittings.

The conduit must be carefully measured before screwing, and after the thread has been cut with the proper dies, the ends must be reamered out to remove all sharp edges.

Steel conduit is made in various sizes, and Table 5 below gives

Table 5. Steel conduit sizes

Conduit external diameter (mm)	Pitch (mm)	Tapping drill (mm)	Clearance drill (mm)
16	1·5	14·5	18
20	1·5	18·5	22
25	1·5	23·5	27
32	1·5	30·5	34

the mechanical characteristics of the sizes most commonly used on domestic installations.

It is laid down in the I.E.E. Regulations that all conduit installations must be completely erected before any wires are drawn in.

In deciding how many wires can be pulled into conduit systems, it must be realised that the heating effect of wires running close together inside a pipe must be taken into account.

The I.E.E. Wiring Regulations lay down the number of separate single-core cables that can be drawn into various sizes of conduit, and it is assumed that the reader who contemplates installing a system of this kind will have consulted the latest edition of the Regulations.

As a guide to typical domestic installations, the following abridged extracts from the Regulations may be given:

Table 6.   Capacities of steel conduits

Nominal conductor size (mm²)	Number of separate cables that may be drawn into conduit of sizes given below							
	Light gauge steel conduit metric (mm)				Heavy gauge metric (mm)			
	16	20	25	32	16	20	25	32
1·0	8	13	22	38	7	12	19	35
1·5	7	12	19	33	6	10	17	31
2·5	5	9	15	26	4	8	13	24
4	3	6	10	17	3	5	9	16
6	3	5	7	13	2	4	7	12

When the cables that are to be run in a particular conduit are of mixed sizes, care must be taken to allow a very considerable amount of free space in the pipe, especially when there are right-angle bends in the run. This is because the heating effect would obviously be intensified if the cables were tightly bunched together.

Installing conduit

In conduit runs, elbows should in general be avoided: bends, made on a proper bending device, should be used instead.

Conduit installations naturally require a considerable amount of equipment by way of stocks and dies for screwing the ends of the piping, portable pipe vices, pipe-bending jigs, and so on. The beginner electrician is unlikely to acquire the full range of tools needed for the installation of various sizes of conduit, and therefore it is not proposed to dwell at length in this book on the details of conduit installation work.

For detailed instructions on the installation of the various types of conduit systems, readers are referred to specialist publications such as *Modern Wiring Practice* by W. E. Steward, published by Newnes-Butterworths.

Sheathed wiring systems

P.V.C. (plastic) insulated and sheathed cables are by far the most commonly used materials in domestic wiring systems, whether for new installations or for extensions to existing wiring.

All wiring systems, as we have seen, must have proper earthing arrangements. With properly screwed metal conduit the conduit itself may act as the earth conductor, but where sheathed cable is used there is usually an uninsulated (bare) wire lying between the red and black live wires within the sheath, to provide earth continuity.

The earth wire provided in a $2 \cdot 5$ mm^2 size twin cable is usually $1 \cdot 5$ mm^2. With larger cables, the earth wire is half the cross-sectional area of the live conductors themselves.

The main points to watch when installing sheathed wiring systems are these:

(a) The greatest possible care must be taken to ensure that the cables are protected against mechanical damage.

(b) The cables have only a limited ability to resist heat, and must not be installed, for example, in the close vicinity of hot-water pipes or near flues.

If cabling has to be run in hot situations, or buried in the ground, the best choice is mineral-insulated copper-sheathed cable.

Preventing mechanical damage

Returning to the question of preventing mechanical damage, the installer must always try to visualise what *might* happen: for example, running a cable in a trough cut into the plaster down a wall to reach the switch may be all right while the present occupier inhabits the room, but it should be realised that some future occupier might easily decide to fit a bookcase or a mirror on that part of the wall, and might drive nails or fixing screws right through the wire. As mentioned in an earlier chapter, metal channelling fitted above the cable before making good the plaster will assist in preventing future operations of this kind from causing trouble.

Similarly, if the floorboards are removed to run cabling beneath, it would be rather tempting, when running at right angles to the joists, to cut a nick, or groove in each joist, and run the cable across them in this way, afterwards replacing the floorboards. But some future occupier, not knowing the run of the cables, might well drive nails or screws into the floor, so penetrating the cable and even causing a fire (see Fig. 4.1).

The proper method is to drill generously sized holes in the joist, at least 50 mm down each joist, and thread the cable through.

In general, if it is difficult to conceal the cables by running through confined spaces, or where thick stone walls are encountered, or if it is very difficult or impossible to obtain access below floors, it is better to run the cabling quite frankly on the surface.

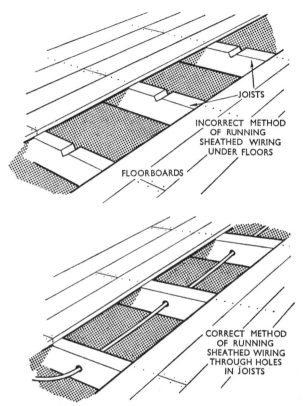

FIG. 4.1. Running cable (or conduit) across joists: it is incorrect to run across the top of the joists in nicks, since nails driven through the floorboards could penetrate the pipe or sheathed cable and cause a fault. This method will also weaken the joists.

People are not likely to damage a cable they can see. It is quite possible to run the usual cables in domestic premises so neatly that when painted to match the surroundings they become almost invisible, but are still apparent to anyone proposing to drill holes or drive nails.

Cables must always be supported by some form of clasp, usually taking the form of plastic clips, the normal spacing being 250 mm apart. Saddles may be used to embrace several cables as shown in Fig. 4.6.

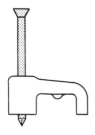

THE PLASTIC CLIP OBTAINABLE IN VARIOUS SIZES, COMPLETE WITH FIXING PIN

FLAT TWIN PVC CABLE WITH EARTH WIRE

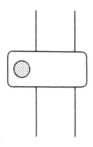

THE CLIP FITTED TO THE CABLE

FIG. 4.2   Installing sheathed wiring: the plastic clip.

The best system to employ, when running out sheathed cables, is to arrange some sort of spindle for the drums, such as a broomstick supported on wooden frames. If the cable runs off the drum as it lies flat on the floor, there will be a danger of producing a twisted mess of cable that will take much time to disentangle and may in any case result in kinks and untidy twists in the cable, preventing a neat appearance in the finished job.

To secure the neatest job, experiment with two short lengths of cable, say 300 mm each, on a piece of wood. See how near to each other the cables will lie, and then apply two sets of plastic clips, 250 mm apart. If the cables are now clipped in, and lie as close together as possible, measure the spacing between the clips at each point, and adopt that measurement along the runs of cable where more than one circuit is to be laid. Nothing looks worse than wiring with two or three cables untidily running along at varying distances apart.

When running out sheathed cable, which comes in 50- or 100-metre drums, great care must be taken to avoid twists and kinks, as mentioned earlier. These may harm the cable if, when kinked, it is pulled too tight. In any case the twists will prevent a neat job being achieved, as it is difficult to smooth them out. The best method to try when endeavouring to smooth out the cable is to clamp a smooth round object of at least 30 mm in diameter in a vice and pull the cable tightly round it, one hand opposing the other.

P.V.C. sheathed cable tends to be stiff to handle in cold weather. This problem can be overcome to some extent by storing the reels in a warm room before operations commence.

Assuming the installation (or extension) is to use sheathed cable run beneath the plaster, the first process is to mark out, as accurately as possible, the cable runs.

The cable will be covered with steel channelling, and this comes in standard sizes. A run commonly used is two 2·5 mm² cables, as employed on a ring circuit, and is about 45 mm wide overall. If this size of channelling is used, a chase, or trough, about 50 mm wide needs to be cut in the plaster.

The best way to cut the plaster without bringing away more

surface than is required is to employ a wide flat chisel and cut diagonally inwards at both sides of the chase. The intervening plaster can then be levered out with a knife.

The cable will terminate in a box, on which will be mounted the switch or socket-outlet.

Steel boxes (Fig. 4.3) are made in two sizes—shallow and deep. The shallow boxes are 16 mm deep, and do not allow much room for more than one cable and the resultant interconnecting wiring.

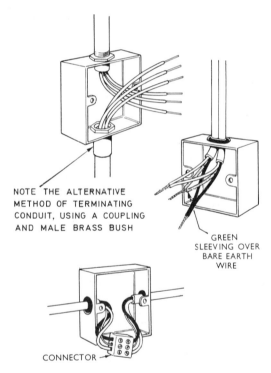

NOTE THE ALTERNATIVE
METHOD OF TERMINATING
CONDUIT, USING A COUPLING
AND MALE BRASS BUSH

GREEN
SLEEVING OVER
BARE EARTH
WIRE

CONNECTOR

Fig. 4.3. Types of box used both on conduit and sheathed-wiring systems showing details and method of baring and twisting the conductors.

It is eminently suitable for switches. The deep box is 38 mm deep, and allows for ample room for P.V.C. connectors, when a joint has to be made in a cable, or for the three sets of wires that result, say, from the entry and exit of ring circuit connections and also the departure of a spur connection.

These boxes have knockouts on all sides, and when the knock-out has been removed, a rubber grommet must be inserted in the hole.

The brickwork must be cut away to receive the deep type of box. This task is eased if an electric drill is available. Over the whole area to be cut away (80 mm square for a one-way box, 80 mm by 160 mm for a two-way, and so on) holes are drilled in the brick with a size 10 or 12 masonry drill, and then a sharp chisel will soon clear away the honeycombed brick (see Fig. 4.4).

The box must be sunk in so that its top edge is about 5 mm below the general plaster level of the wall.

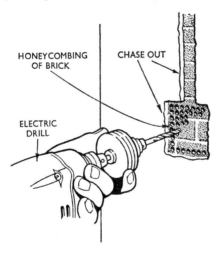

HONEYCOMBING
OF BRICK

CHASE OUT

ELECTRIC
DRILL

Fig. 4.4. Using the electric drill to prepare the brick-work for the large hole needed for a deep box. Speed reduction gear is necessary for drills with a speed above 500 rev/min.

Holes for screws will be found in the base of the box, two of them usually being oval to allow for adjustment. Holes must now be drilled in the wall (a size 6 woodscrew is usually used, so an appropriate drill or bit must be used) and the box screwed firmly to the brick.

At this point a small spirit-level is useful, because the levelling of the box will ensure that the front plate of the switch or socket-outlet will also come out exactly level. If one switch-plate slopes one way and an adjacent switch slopes in the opposite direction, the result clearly indicates bad workmanship. The spirit-level may be used to level the box, using the tolerance provided by the oval holes, before the screws are finally tightened.

On any side of the box where cables are to enter, the brickwork should be chamfered away as shown in Fig. 4.5, so that there is a smooth slope and not a sharp edge.

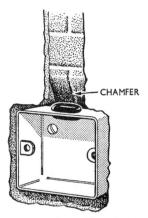

CHAMFER

FIG. 4.5. Chamfering away of brickwork to allow smooth entry into a cable box.

The next step is to run the cables in the chase cut in the plaster. The cables are naturally springy, and it is not easy to get them to be flat ready to receive the metal channelling. It has been found worthwhile to plug the brick in one or two places (easily accomplished with an electric drill) and to fit a few clips along the run to hold the cables in position (see Fig. 4.6).

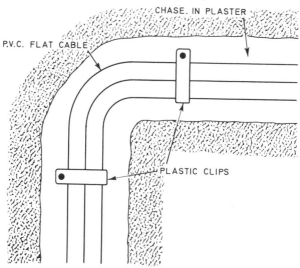

CHASE. IN PLASTER

P.V.C. FLAT CABLE

PLASTIC CLIPS

FIG. 4.6. It is of assistance, when installing metal channelling, to keep the cable flat against the wall by using plastic clips under the channelling.

Note. The radius of the sharpest bend must be at least four times the overall diameter of the cable (too tight a bend will damage the P.V.C.). Also, all hidden cable should be run either vertically or horizontally, to give indication of run.

The channelling may be secured by tacks or screws. Sometimes a satisfactory fixing (bearing in mind that the plaster will soon hold the channelling firmly) may be secured by tacks driven into the crevices between bricks. But the springy nature of P.V.C.-insulated cable, especially, will often mean that screws, driven into proper plugged holes, say every 300 mm along each edge of the channelling, will have to be employed to secure a neat job in which the channelling is properly sunk well below the plaster level.

The channelling should be cut so that it forms a continuous cover for the cable. This means that it comes right up to each box. Sharp edges should be filed so that there is no danger of subsequent pressure accidentally cutting through the insulation.

The cables cannot be made off into the boxes before the wall is ' made good '—plastered and painted. Otherwise the switches and other fittings could become covered in paint.

The next step is to make good the plaster. The best method is to use first a cement and sand mixture (half cement, half sand) to fill in the main part of the trough containing the cables and their protective channelling, right up to the normal plaster surface layer.

An important point to remember here is that if the cement is allowed to harden for too long, it will be difficult to rake away the top layer to allow for subsequent plastering to restore the smooth unbroken surface of the original wall. Therefore the cement layer should be given, say, not more than 2 days to set, and then the surface should be scraped so that it lies about 5 mm below the normal wall level. The final finishing coat of plaster can then be applied. Priming and final painting can follow when the plaster has fully dried out.

THE LAYOUT PLAN

An important factor to consider is the situation of the intake point. One place to avoid is the cupboard under the stairs, which is likely to get filled with things like pushchairs and tennis racquets, so that (a) the meter reader has great difficulty in getting to the meter, and (b) if a fuse blows, confusion in the resulting darkness may become even greater as the householder first has to force his way through old trunks and then fumble with fuseboard covers on his knees.

It should be realised that the Area Electricity Boards only allow a certain distance of ' free ' cable, from the mains in the street, or from the pole line, to the supply point. This is often of the order of 10 metres. If a supply point position is chosen so that this distance is exceeded, the consumer must be prepared to pay for the extra cable involved.

Where a garage adjoins the house, this is often found to be a convenient place for the intake point, but care must be taken (a) to situate the fuses, etc., in a position agreed with the Area Electricity Board, and (b) to allow ample room for cabling runs to the rest of the house, *and* for extensions to the fuseboard assembly.

Another good place for the meter and the fuseboards is in a cupboard over the side door. The meter reader will not have to tramp all through the house, on a muddy day, and all that is necessary in general is for anyone to stand on a chair to obtain easy access to the fuses. A torch—or even a candle—will give a good light in this position, and a candle will not be dangerous.

Many new houses are fitted with a cloakroom or lavatory adjacent to the hall, and this is another place where the intake point may conveniently be situated, perhaps in a cupboard.

The number of socket-outlets to be installed, and their positions, must be a matter for the individual choice of the owner of the installation, but the electrician should try and persuade him to be as generous as possible with outlets. In every household the usage of electrical appliances is always increasing.

A reasonable number of socket-outlets for a three-bedroomed semi-detached house is indicated in Fig. 3.13 (page 60).

In general socket-outlets should be installed in living rooms at about 500 mm from the floor level, to obviate the need to stoop down to insert the plug. In the kitchen, socket-outlets may be at table-top level, for convenience in using irons, food mixers, kettles and the like.

It is desirable to install at least one socket-outlet on the landing and another in the hall, so that vacuum-cleaner connections may be made without difficulty.

It should always be remembered that much time and material can be saved by careful planning and measuring-up before commencing work. The frenzied rush to the electrical shop for one more reel of cable, just as it closes, is the hall-mark of the amateur.

There is another advantage in taking great care to prepare a drawn-out plan of the installation. It is almost inevitable that extensions will be needed some time in the future, and it is of course not impossible that a fault will occur in some part of the wiring. If the original wiring plan is available, both the work of extension and that of tracing and rectifying a fault will be greatly simplified.

Identifying tags attached to cables under floors and behind fuseboards will be found useful if work is carried out in the future.

GENERAL HINTS ON INSTALLATION WORK
Conduit wiring

If conduit wiring is to be installed, the conduit must be placed in position at exactly the right time in relation to the other building work, or else there will be a great deal of expensive reinstatement of plaster work that has had to be cut into to run the conduit. This stage is usually called the carcassing stage.

When the shell of the house is built, and the roof is on, but before the floorboards are laid and of course before plastering commences, the electrician has the ideal conditions for his work. In an ordinary three-bedroomed semi-detached house an electrician and his mate should be able to complete the first stage of the wiring in a week.

Conduit is run on the walls and it is usually necessary to chase out a trough in the brickwork for the conduit to lie partly below the surface, otherwise, with a plaster depth of only 10 mm, the conduit would stand proud of the wall. For the outlet boxes, into which the actual socket-outlets are to be fitted, a deeper hole must be cut in the wall.

Under the floors, the conduit should not be on top of the joists in a vee-nick cut for the purpose. This is bad practice as a heavy nail could easily be driven through the pipe. The best method is to drill with an auger a hole at least 50 mm down each joist (if running across the joists) and thread the conduit through these holes. If running with the joists, the conduit should be held by saddles about half-way up the joist.

Right-angle elbows should be avoided wherever possible, because of the obstacle they provide to easy drawing-in of the wires. Bends are preferred, and these should have an internal radius of not less than 2·5 times the overall diameter of the conduit, e.g. overall diameter of conduit=16 mm, minimum internal radius of bend=16×2·5=40 mm.

Although a conduit system is in theory completely sealed, from end to end, air can gain access at the socket-outlets and switches, and moisture-carrying air brings with it the danger of condensation. This could mean that small quantities of water could run down into switches and other fittings, and give rise to corrosion. To prevent this, conduit systems should have drain holes situated at low points (preferably in boxes).

Conduit runs should always be kept clear of gas pipes, water pipes, and any other wiring. This is because of the possible dangers of bimetallic corrosion through contact between different metals, and also because of possible sparking dangers, if a fault should occur on the electrical installation and fault current flows through the conduit itself.

As erection proceeds, draw wires should be inserted from junction box to junction box. These wires (or flat steel tapes) will greatly facilitate drawing-in. It will be remembered that the Regulations provide that all the conduit must be complete before any wires are drawn in.

When conduit piping is cut, the cut ends must have all burrs removed by means of a suitable rose bit attached to a drill.

When pulling in the cables, the best method is to bare all the ends of the conductors, twist them together and bend them over to form an eye and attach the end of the fish wire or tape to this eye. The procedure is shown in Fig. 4.7. Care must be taken later to cut away the whole of the conductors used for this purpose, as they may have become damaged, before making them off into the fittings.

Always make certain that enough cable is pulled through. It is very unwise to leave only the bare minimum protruding from the box in the wall. If any slight slip is made during making off, there will be an extremely arduous business of pulling new wire

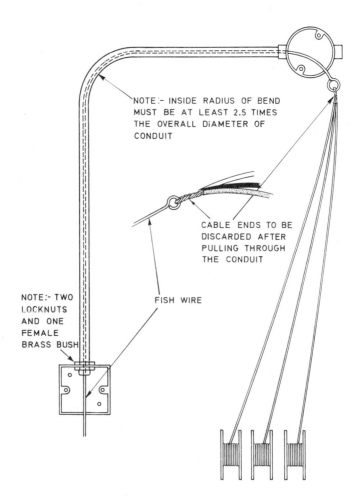

NOTE:- INSIDE RADIUS OF BEND
MUST BE AT LEAST 2.5 TIMES
THE OVERALL DiAMETER OF
CONDUIT

CABLE ENDS TO BE
DISCARDED AFTER
PULLING THROUGH
THE CONDUIT

NOTE:- TWO
LOCKNUTS
AND ONE
FEMALE
BRASS BUSH

FISH WIRE

FIG. 4.7. Use of fish wire and twisted cables when pulling into conduit. The twisted end must be discarded before connecting up, as it may become damaged.

in, and this may be made more difficult still if plastering has been carried out and has to be broken away to get access to the junction boxes.

As a general rule, always try to avoid joints. This means, of course, that short lengths of cable will get left on drums, and the electrician may think he has been wasteful. But he will have the satisfaction of knowing he has provided a sound job, and he will have avoided the laborious business of making joints in junction boxes which may—and often do—find themselves in difficult positions.

When it is necessary to pull in a number of cables, nasty kinks and knots may be avoided by 'combing' the cables through a piece of wood or stiff cardboard, with an appropriate number of holes, before entering them into the conduit. This will ensure that the cables are reasonably straight and will ease the drawing in process.

Sheathed wiring systems

With sheathed wiring systems, using the two-core and earth arrangement, the overriding principle that the electrician must always bear in mind is to prevent the cables from encountering mechanical damage.

The best way of running sheathed wiring in plaster is to install a round or oval conduit for all runs, or at the least to chase out a trough for the wiring so that it can be covered with a metal channel. The use of conduit for runs to socket-outlets and switches had the advantage of enabling the cable to be pulled out if it has to be replaced, without breaking away the wall.

The normal way of securing sheathed wiring, as mentioned earlier, is by means of saddle clips, usually every 200 mm. Where a cable runs under floors it is even more important than with conduit not to run them in nicks out of the top of the joists, since these cables are much more vulnerable to nails than conduit. Again, the correct method is to run the cables through holes drilled in each joist. A portable electric drill, fitted with a proper wood-boring tool, can easily cut 20 mm holes in joists, and this size of hole will allow for at least three 2·5 mm² cables.

Where a number of cables run *along* a joist, half-way down, an easy way of fixing is to use saddles from old sheath ends, secured with tacks of at least 15 mm in length.

Sheathed cables should never be allowed to run unsupported for a distance much exceeding 300 mm. The reason for this is that if they are at any time subjected to overheating—and this may be due not only to the passage of excess current, but also through the proximity of a flue, or a hot-water pipe—the sagging cable may become distorted so that the P.V.C. insulation tends to drop away from the conductors, and might even leave them bare.

It is always bad practice to tie or tape sheathed cables to existing water or gas pipes—especially the latter. Wood battens should be run along the path to be taken by the cables, well removed from the piping, and the cables properly secured by means of saddle clips.

Where sheathed cables have to pass through a wall, or through any partition, the best method is to use some lengths of protective conduit (see Fig. 4.8). If this is not done a sharp edge in the

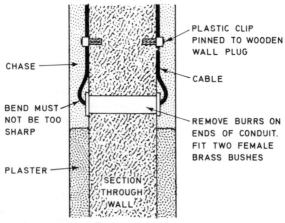

FIG. 4.8. Running sheathed cable through walls: protective conduit should be employed, it need not be earthed.

brickwork may gradually work its way into the cable, causing a fault which is awkward to find and even more awkward to repair.

Where the wiring need not be covered for aesthetic reasons, such as in a garage, it is better to run it in such a way that it can be clearly seen (Fig. 4.9). By using this method damage to the wiring will be less likely than if it is indifferently concealed. No one in their senses cuts or damages an electric cable that can be seen.

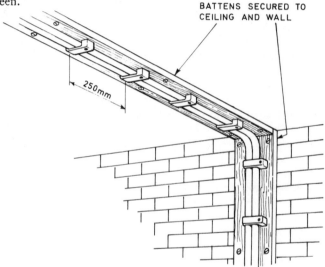

BATTENS SECURED TO CEILING AND WALL

250 mm

FIG. 4.9. Sheathed wiring run bare on battens, as, for example, in a garage.

It is always worth while to arrange that junction boxes occur below screwed traps in the floorboards, for easy access. Junction boxes must never be left unsupported except by the cable itself— a fault commonly found. The box must be firmly screwed to the nearest fixed surface.

Making off the cable ends

Perhaps the most likely source of trouble in an electrical installation lies in bad workmanship when making off cable ends.

When baring the insulation from the conductors, savage tearing with a sharp knife may easily cut through or nick one or more strands of wire, and these loose pieces of wire may come adrift and cause short-circuits, or may reduce the current-carrying capacity at the terminal, and so cause overheating.

When bringing two (or more) conductors into a terminal, enough insulation should be bared from each to allow the wires to be twisted together, with only enough bare copper showing for proper insertion in the terminal. The wires may be twisted with flat-nosed pliers, and then the twisted ends cut off neatly with side cutters.

Only practice and experience will show exactly how much length of single conductor should be left outside the cable sheath, and of this, how much should be bared to make the connection. If too much wire is bared, there is a danger that as the box is closed up, the wires may become twisted or compressed against each other so that short-circuits occur. If on the other hand too little ' tail ' wire (wire outside the sheath) is made available, making off may be difficult, and this may lead to the physical impossibility of tightening all the terminals as they should be tightened.

Loosely tightened terminals can easily cause internal sparking and overheating. An element of high resistance is introduced into the circuit at this point, and insulation may become charred and dangerous, and springs in switch contacts may become overheated and lose their tension, and so provoke further trouble.

As each fitting—switch, ceiling rose, or socket-outlet—is completed, it should be *gently* pushed into position, the electrician taking every opportunity to make absolutely certain that as the fitting goes into its box none of the wires is being twisted too sharply, or compressed against a sharp edge, or brought into too close contact with the live terminals.

5

ACCESSORIES AND FITTINGS

THE FUSEBOARD

Starting at the fuseboard (Fig. 5.1) where the installer's responsibility commences, this component should be chosen with considerable care with two viewpoints in mind:

   (i) Ease of installation of the original wiring.

   (ii) Ease of adding new wiring when the occasion demands.

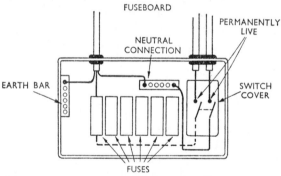

FIG. 5.1. The interior of a typical fuseboard, showing phase connection, neutral connection, earth bar and the cover over the switch, whose terminals remain alive even when the switch is off.

For an average domestic installation, the fuseboard assembly might well include an eight-way fuseboard, 30 amperes each way, allocated as follows:

   Two for the two ring circuits.

   One for the cooker circuit.

One for the main water-heating immersion heater.
One for a 3-kilowatt fixed radiator in the living room.
Two for lighting circuits (fused at 5 amperes each).
One spare.

But there will be many variants: no two types of installation will have exactly the same needs.

As mentioned earlier in this book on several occasions, careful studies concerning diversity of use, carried out over many years in many different types of household using various kinds of appliance, have shown that it is safe to allow for considerable diversity: in other words, to plan the wiring and fuses and other appliances on the basis that not all the potential, or possible, loading will occur at the same time.

For example, in the I.E.E. Wiring Regulations, for individual domestic installations, the *suggested* diversity factor that can be applied for example, to fixed heating and power appliances other than motors, cookers and water heaters is 100% full load up to 10 amperes, and above that 50% of any load in excess of 10 amperes.

Taking this suggestion as a guide, if in a four-bedroomed house there are 2-kilowatt fixed electric fires in each bedroom, the total potential loading would be $4 \times 2 = 8$ kilowatts $= 33 \cdot 28$ amperes. But the diversity factor suggested means that the cable size could be proportioned for the first 10 amperes plus 50% of the remaining current $(33 \cdot 28 - 10 = 23 \cdot 28$ amperes) or $11 \cdot 64$ amperes. In total, therefore, the current that should be allowed for is $10 + 11 \cdot 64 = 21 \cdot 64$ amperes, instead of $33 \cdot 28$ amperes. This also applies to the fuses and the other fittings.

However, it must be emphasised that this (and other suggested diversity factors) are only guides. The person responsible for the installation must make his own judgement.

For example, while for a cooker the same kind of diversity factor is suggested, if this cooker is installed, say, in a nursing home where special meals are prepared, or in a large house where a large family lives, or perhaps in a small café, the diversity factor does not necessarily apply.

The worst that can happen if too *large* a cable and fuseboard are installed is some small, *apparently* unnecessary expense at the time of installation.

The worst that can happen if too *small* a cable and fuseboard are installed are overheating (with possible fire danger), frequent blowing of fuses, and a probable need to embark on a costly and inconvenient programme of rewiring.

Each fuseboard will have its own main switch, fuseholders for each way, and neutral terminals and earth terminals.

There are metal-clad and insulated enclosures for fuseboards. If a conduit system is being installed, a metal-clad fuseboard will be used. For sheathed cable systems, the insulated enclosure is more usual, but the metal-clad type may be used if desired, care of course being taken to ensure that the metal enclosure is properly earthed.

All fuseboards are provided with knockouts. These are either sheet-metal plugs, pressed into holes appropriate for conduit or wire entry, or else (in plastic boxes) clearly defined thin places in the plastic case, which can be tapped out by a careful tap with a hammer.

The Regulations state that fuseboards (and indeed all enclosures surrounding live parts) must be completely closed. This is required to prevent the ingress of moisture, insects, and dust. So if any knockouts are not required for wiring they must be left intact, or if already knocked out, closed by means of rubber plugs.

Where conduit enters a fuseboard it must be fitted with a smooth brass bush at its end, to prevent the wires being abraded on the rough edges of the pipe. When bringing sheathed wiring into fuseboards, close-fitting rubber grommets must always be used. These grommets have the dual purpose of protecting the wiring from damage when passing through the rough edges of the hole, and also blocking the hole around the wiring to seal the interior of the box.

Fuseboards may be installed, in general, straight on to a brick or concrete wall (see Fig. 5.2). But there are several disadvantages if this method is used. First, brick walls may be damp, and this will ultimately cause rusting, even on the best galvanised

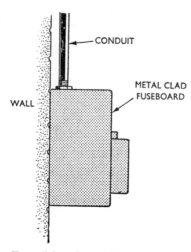

FIG. 5.2.   Installation of fuseboards directly on wall, showing
conduit entries from above.

boxes. Secondly, to obtain the neatest wiring layout, particularly
with sheathed wiring, it is desirable to bring the wiring in from
the back of the fuseboard, and this is not possible if the boxes
are flush against the wall. (For conduit wiring, top entry is
usually more convenient.)

The ideal method is to make up (or obtain ready-made) a
strong wooden board, of not less than 13 mm timber, supported
on battens at either side so that it stands about 50 mm away
from the wall (see Fig. 5.3). This board is then firmly fixed to
the wall at its left and right edges. The sheathed wiring, brought
in from above on battens, can then be taken into the fuseboards
through holes of generous size (not less than 20 mm diameter)
drilled in the board at points carefully measured out to coincide
with the back knockouts in the insulated fuseboards.

With ample space behind the wooden board, the wiring will
not be unduly pinched up, so avoiding the possibility of damage
and overheating. Moreover, new wiring can easily be added.

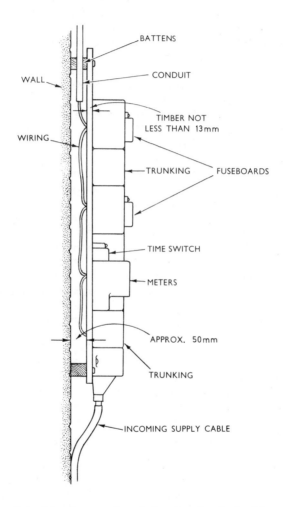

FIG. 5.3. A meter board showing sheathed cable entering from behind the fuseboard.

Further holes can be drilled in the baseboard by removing the fixing screws of any one fuseboard, and—if proper slack has been left in the wiring behind the board—slightly moving it out of place so that the hole can be drilled and the new wire brought through.

For installations of a size larger than the smallest domestic supplies, the Area Electricity Board often provide the form of consumer's termination unit in which the supply cable sealing box, the main fuses, and the meter are mounted in such a way that a trunking connection may be made directly to the consumer's fuseboards, with the fuseboards mounted, as it were, on top of and in direct touch with the trunking. (See Fig. 1.7, page 25.)

It should always be remembered that space should be provided on the baseboard for possible additional fuseboards. For example, if off-peak storage heating is to be added, not only will an extra fuseboard be needed, but a time-switch and possibly a contactor will have to be installed.

Again, if the size of the installation grows so that a 3-phase supply main has to be brought in, there will be the need for separate fuseboards for each phase; and if this move has been necessitated by the installation of off-peak storage heating, there will have to be fuseboards for the red, yellow and blue phases on-peak, and for the red, yellow and blue phases off-peak, making six in all.

As a final addition, if for example the immersion heater for the hot water needs of the house is not to be controlled by the weather-conscious thermostat that may be installed to control the off-peak storage heating, then a separate single-phase fuseboard will be needed for that circuit alone (see Fig. 5.4).

WIRING ACCESSORIES

In running out the wiring from the fuseboard, one cardinal principle must always be observed. There should if at all possible be no joints in the wiring runs other than those made at proper fittings, using screw-down terminals of suitable size.

For conduit systems, the joint in the actual wiring is made in

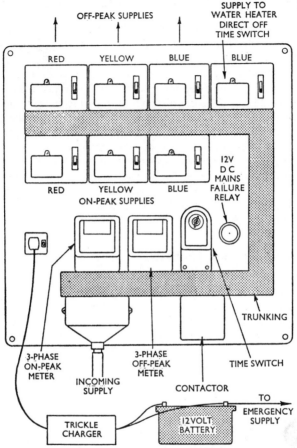

FIG. 5.4. A complete layout, as installed in the author's own home, with trunking joining the fuseboards to the meters and time-switch, and with a 3-phase supply for both off-peak and on-peak circuits. The fourth fuseboard on the off-peak row is for immersion water heater supplies which are not separately controlled by the anticipatory thermostat installed outside the building to control the off-peak storage heating. This fuseboard receives its supply directly from the time-switch. The installation also includes 12-volt emergency lighting system with a trickle charger, so that in the event of power failure a number of 12-volt lamps automatically become alight.

joint boxes fitted into the conduit run. Inside the joint box there
must be a porcelain or plastic connector, containing screw-down
brass terminals or connecting pieces.

Care must always be taken to avoid what is unfortunately a
common device for fixing more wires into a terminal than it will
properly hold, or wires larger than those for which it was designed.
Many amateurs have been known to cut away several of the
bared strands of the conductors, to make them fit into the
terminal. This practice is entirely wrong, and may well be highly
dangerous. The reduced copper section at this one point may
well give rise to considerable overheating, without blowing any
fuse, and it could therefore happen that a fire is caused through
the whole junction box (or switch or fuseboard or socket-outlet)
becoming red hot.

Connection or junction boxes

With sheathed wiring systems, junction, or connection boxes,
usually of a round shape, are available. The electrician must be
certain that the terminals are large enough to contain the required
number (usually two, but sometimes three, at a tee-off point) of
wires of the size to be used.

It should be mentioned, however, that many of these connection
boxes are only suitable for use with the smaller sizes of cable,
usually less than the 2·5 mm² size. Some connection boxes are
specially made to take three 2·5 mm² conductors, for example
where a tee-off is required.

The best practice is to avoid connection boxes wherever possible. Lighting circuits may be looped in, using four-plate
ceiling roses, to avoid the necessity for joints (as mentioned later
in this chapter) and, on ring main circuits, any tee-off connections
ought if possible to be made at socket-outlets, since the terminals
on these units are capable of carrying three 2·5 mm² conductors.

Connection boxes are designed with knockout sections, and
these should be broken out in such a way that the cable fits
snugly and does not allow empty spaces around it where dust and
insects may penetrate.

Where there is considerable likelihood that moisture or fumes or dust will penetrate, the proper box to use is a conduit type with sealing glands (that can be bought from the cable suppliers) so that the cable is properly sealed in to the box entry holes.

Metal boxes for switches, socket-outlets, etc., should be used with sheathed wiring systems, although plastic-type boxes are available. If metal boxes are used, the earth wire brought in with the cable must make proper connection with the box itself. An earthing screw is sometimes provided for this purpose, but the socket-outlet or other device usually has an internal arrangement whereby the earth connection terminal on the socket-outlet body has a metal strap connecting it to the screws used to fix the device on to the box, thus providing an earth connection when the socket-outlet is assembled.

A short cut sometimes adopted by amateurs, where they wish to earth a metal box, is to trap the earth wire beneath the lid of the box, holding it tight by means of the fixing screws. This means that a gap is left, through which moisture may penetrate. This short cut should not be employed.

Where plastic boxes are used, care must be taken to see that holes are not left in such a way that subsequent plastering will cause the box to become filled with liquid plaster.

Whatever type of box is used, it should be chosen so that there is ample room for all the wiring, and that when the switch or other fitment is applied, the wiring will not be squeezed up so tight that there is danger of a sharp point on the back of the switch pressing the wires against the metal part, with the possibility of ultimate breakdown of the insulation.

There is another danger that must be carefully avoided, and that is of cutting off the ends of the cable a fraction too short, so that when the switch is pressed home and the retaining screws are tightened, one or other of the connections is being gradually strained either to breaking point or else to the point where it is pulled out of the terminal.

Only experiment and practice on a dummy circuit, using some scrap cable, will show how much cable should be left.

All fittings—boxes, surface switches, socket-outlets and the like—must allow for the outer sheath of the cable, in sheathed cable systems, to be brought well inside the protection of the box—in other words, the unprotected cores of the cable, even with their normal insulation, must never be accessible outside an area protected by some form of box.

Ceiling roses and connectors

Ceiling roses, for pendant lamps, are nowadays made in plastic with non-inflammable back plates, called patresses.

These ceiling roses often have four terminals instead of the three that might be expected. This is because many electricians use the loop-in system (Fig. 5.5), which uses a little more wire but involves less labour than the alternative.

The loop-in system has the advantage of not requiring a

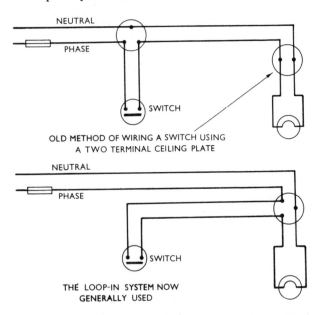

FIG. 5.5. The loop-in system for ceiling rose wiring. Earth continuity conductor omitted for clarity.

junction box at the point shown in the figure, and further that it does not need a joint to be made at all. If, however, there is some good reason for using the joint box, the connection that has to be made inside it must be carried out by the use of a proper porcelain or plastic clad connector.

There is a type of connector that may be found very useful, if properly applied, in situations such as that mentioned above. The ' Scruit ' (patented) type connector is made in a number of sizes, and the correct size must always be used. Care must be taken not to allow any bare wires to appear outside the acorn-shaped porcelain, and after the porcelain has been screwed firmly home on the wires, that have been bared and twisted together, the whole may be firmly wrapped with one or two turns of black insulating tape or plastic tape—one of the few instances where insulating tape may legitimately be used on a permanent installation: it is not employed as insulation, but simply to assist in ensuring that the Scruit connector is kept tight (see Fig. 5.6).

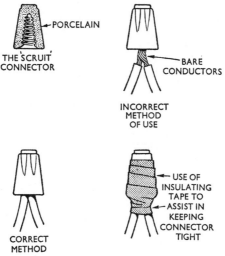

FIG. 5.6. The ' Scruit ' connector in use.

Connection of fixed appliances

For the connection of fixed appliances, several methods may be adopted. With conduit systems, a flexible metallic conduit may be used to bridge the gap between the free-standing appliance and the fixed terminal box recessed into the wall. The lid of the terminal box may be drilled to receive the bushed end of the flexible conduit.

With sheathed systems this method can still be used, but in this case great care must be taken to ensure that the flexible conduit is properly earthed to the earth wire in the cable; and it is also desirable, in any case, to run a separate earth wire inside the flexible conduit, since after a long period of use the flexible conduit may conceivably rust and break through, thus leaving the appliance with no earth connection.

The normal method of connecting most fixed appliances, with sheathed cable systems, is to use a fused spur box with a special flexible cable outlet, the cable employed being chosen to be suitable for the job in hand, i.e. a heat-resisting cable for connection to an appliance generating heat.

Other appliances, such as fluorescent lamp fittings and towel rails, for example, are generally provided with bases of such a type that either they will fit directly on to the standard galvanised steel conduit termination box, or else they fit on to the wall or ceiling in such a way that they form a complete enclosure over the properly bushed end of the conduit, or of the protected end of the sheathed cable, *and* at the same time are provided with proper means for securing the earth connections.

On ring main circuits, as we have seen earlier, a limited number of spur connections are permitted, and for this purpose spur boxes, both fused and unfused are available.

The fused spur box can be made available either in the flush or surface type, and can be mounted in standard conduit boxes.

The unfused spur is basically a connecting box with a switch, with ample room for the three wires that go on each terminal—the wires from either side of the ring, and the spur.

SPECIAL FITTINGS

Clock connectors

For clocks, where the current consumption is very small indeed, special fused clock connectors may be used. These moulded plastic appliances are neat and small, but do not usually permit of their being mounted straight into a ring main, as the terminals are too small for the ring-type conductors. They are often connected into a convenient lighting circuit, where smaller conductors are used. A 2-ampere fuse is incorporated.

Outlets for fixed storage heaters

As socket-outlets are not permitted on off-peak circuits for off-peak storage heaters a fused spur box type of fitting is used, even though the mains connection is not made to a ring main but directly back to the off-peak main fuseboard. A 13-ampere type of fitting, with the appropriate fuse, is usually employed, and may be of the flush type, or may be installed on the surface. Heat-resisting flexible leads must be used for the final connection to the heater.

A special problem may arise in connection with those storage heaters that are fitted with fans to boost the heat output when needed. Since the boost is needed at on-peak times as well as during off-peak hours these fans must obviously operate from a normal, or on-peak circuit. Therefore the separate circuit within the appliance that feeds the fan needs connecting to a normal on-peak socket-outlet (see Fig. 5.7).

But since many domestic installations nowadays, where off-peak heating is fitted, are fed on the 3-phase system, it is necessary to ensure that two different phase connections are not brought near to each other in the same room. This would mean that a voltage above low voltage could exist, and the possibility of a fatal shock would be increased.

This requirement means that when the off-peak storage heating is installed the electrical layout of the installation as a whole must be considered. It may not be found very difficult to rearrange the main circuits at the fuseboard so that, for

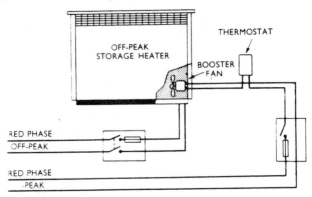

Fig. 5.7. Connection diagram of storage heater with fan, showing the need to connect both the storage heater circuit and the fan circuit to the same phase, although not to the same fuseboard. The two switches should be mechanically interlinked, so that the heater is completely isolated in one operation.

example, the two storage heaters that are situated on the ground floor are both fed from the red phase off-peak circuit, while the ground floor ring for on-peak socket-outlets is also fed from the red phase. On the first floor, the blue phase may be used both for the first floor ring and for the off-peak storage heaters.

Floor-mounted socket-outlets

Many manufacturers provide a special type of floor socket-outlet, fitted with a strong cover that may be screwed into place when the plug is not in use, so that no dust or moisture can find its way into the fitting, and furniture can be confidently allowed to stand on it. Such a special fitting should always be used when the circumstances make it necessary.

Outdoor fittings

To prevent (a) ingress of rain, and (b) condensation inside, specially designed weatherproof switches, socket-outlets, lamp-holders and all other fittings should always be used outdoors.

Galvanised steel conduit boxes should be used, even if conduit is not being employed, since sheathed cable can be brought into these boxes, in a watertight fashion, by means of the special glands that can be supplied by the manufacturers. If there is any doubt about watertightness, most cable manufacturers supply a type of plastic compound that remains flexible indefinitely, and may be used to plug the intake ends of the cables coming into outdoor-mounted fittings.

Switches may be purchased in a weatherproof form, usually mounted in cast-iron boxes. Great care must be taken in bringing in either conduit or sheathed cable (with glands) to see (a) that earthing continuity is carefully preserved, and (b) that no moisture can enter, whatever the direction of the rain.

It is desirable that outdoor boxes, such as those containing switches, should have a very small hole on the underside, well protected from the weather, to allow for condensation water to escape. To prevent the ingress of insects through this hole, a small piece of fine mesh wire grid may be secured over the hole, inside the box.

Bathroom switches

It is contrary to the Regulations that there should be any portable electrical appliance or socket-outlet (except shaver sockets to BS 3052) or switch other than that of the ceiling type in a bathroom, and all electrical fittings must be of the all-insulated type: that is, the outer body must contain no metal parts at all. All lampholders used in bathrooms must be of the all-insulated type, and must be fitted with a protective skirt, as illustrated in Fig. 5.8.

The two most commonly used special fittings for bathrooms are the shaver socket and the ceiling switch.

Shaver sockets

To ensure that no user of an electric razor could receive a shock while shaving in wet conditions, specially designed shaver sockets must be used.

Shaver sockets use a small transformer, the secondary side of which—the side that supplies the razor itself—is entirely isolated from earth, so that no one touching any part of this circuit could receive an electric shock, as there would be no return path to earth.

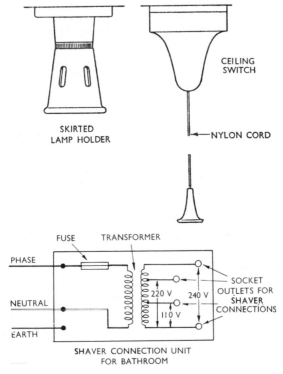

SKIRTED
LAMP HOLDER

CEILING
SWITCH

NYLON CORD

FUSE   TRANSFORMER

PHASE

220 V   240 V

NEUTRAL

110 V

EARTH

SOCKET
OUTLETS FOR
SHAVER
CONNECTIONS

SHAVER CONNECTION UNIT
FOR BATHROOM

FIG. 5.8. Bathroom fittings. Comprising special shaver
socket, lampholder with skirt, and ceiling switch.

Only shaver sockets which comply with British Standard 3052
(which lays down the standard of insulation between the primary
and secondary windings of the isolation transformer, and specifies
other safety precautions) may be used in bathrooms, and they
must be properly earthed.

Ceiling switches

For bathrooms one way of complying with the Regulations is
to place the lighting switches outside the room altogether, and

this practice is often adopted. A single light may be switched in this way, and another light, say over a mirror, may well be switched by means of a ceiling switch. This type of switch is mounted on the ceiling and operated by means of a pull cord, usually of nylon. Some such switches have an indicator light, so they may be found in the dark.

Apparatus installed in inflammable atmospheres

If electrical apparatus is to be brought anywhere near an area where petrol, paraffin, butane gas, or any inflammable substance is used, or where the vapour that rises from such substances may persist, then various Regulations made by Local Authorities must be obeyed, and these Regulations, added to the I.E.E. Regulations, impose a very high standard of practice in such situations.

To start with, specially designed apparatus must be used. This is known as flame-proof gear, and it is rigidly tested to ensure not only that sparks cannot escape and cause explosions, but in addition it is so arranged that if inflammable gases are trapped inside the conduits or boxes, and an internal explosion occurs, the metal parts will resist it and will not cause bare electrical wires to be exposed.

The beginner is advised not to contemplate the installation of flame-proof gear unless he has professional advice available, and in addition he must be sure that he has studied—and complied with—the stringent Regulations that apply.

Bell transformers

We shall see later that all circuits such as extra low voltage bell wiring, television and sound radio, aerials, loudspeaker connections, and telephone wiring must be kept quite separate from power wiring, and must not be run in the same conduit or trunking.

There is however one point where the extra low voltage and standard systems meet. Electrical bells and chimes are often supplied up to 14 volts by means of small transformers, fed from the mains.

Such transformers are usually supplied by fused spur connections from a convenient lighting circuit, and may be fused at 2 amperes. Some bell transformers have their own fuses inside the case. Care must be taken to ensure that the 14-volt circuit wires cannot possibly come into contact with the 240-volt mains circuit unless the bell circuit is insulated for the higher voltage. Auto-transformers (mentioned under 'Transformers', p. 163) must not be employed.

Double-pole switches

We have seen earlier that with the phase and neutral supply system (not necessarily with non-standard systems) the switches used other than the main switches at the fuseboards, are of the single-pole type—that is, they break the phase conductor only, and not the neutral.

But there are some exceptions to this rule. In the case of immersion heaters the Regulations lay down that double-pole switches shall be used; and for any *fixed* heating appliance *where the heating elements could possibly be touched*, both conductors feeding the appliance must be interrupted by a switch placed near the appliance (see Fig. 5.9). (This would apply for example, to a glowing-bar type radiator permanently installed on a wall,

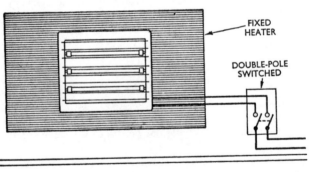

FIG. 5.9.   Double-pole switches used for fixed heating appliances.

which must have a wire screen to prevent a coat or dress blowing up against it, but where the elements could be touched by inquiring childish fingers when the fire appears to be safe as it is not glowing.)

Double-pole switches are available from all manufacturers for these special applications, and will mostly fit into the same boxes (or occupy the same space as surface units) as their single-pole counterparts.

6

EXTENSIONS TO OLD INSTALLATIONS AND TEMPORARY WIRING

EXTENSIONS TO OLD INSTALLATIONS

THE beginner electrician is probably called on to carry out extensions to old installations much more frequently than to install complete new wiring.

The Supply Authority reserves the right to be notified of any proposed addition to an existing installation, for a number of reasons. First, they must be satisfied that their service cable and meter will not become overloaded. Secondly, they must ensure that any additional connections do not disturb the service to other consumers. (For example, a heavy load, suddenly imposed or removed on a single-phase supply at the end of a long main cable, might cause severe flicker on the lighting systems of all the nearby consumers. Finally, they must test the extension, to ensure that it is safe in every way.)

Extending or repairing old installations may offer many more traps than new work.

The electrician, called on to install, say, a new power point in an old house, must first satisfy himself as to the state of the existing wiring. In a later section on testing we shall discuss this matter more fully, but it may be mentioned here that the first test is to see that the main fuseboard is not already overloaded, according to the principles set out in an earlier chapter about the loading of the various circuits; and then he must check the insulation of the existing wiring and its earthing condition.

Too often, in old houses, the wiring (perhaps 30 or 40 years old, and carried out in rubber-insulated wire) has severely deteriorated. The rubber insulation has become brittle and broken in places, and where overheating has occurred (especially at such places as ceiling roses where larger and larger lamps have continually been employed, over the years), the insulation may be in a very poor condition. This may not always be fully revealed with the ' Megger ' test for insulation (see chapter on testing), but such a test should be accompanied by a visual inspection of the wiring in a typical fitting. In such cases, no extensions should be added to such wiring, and the householder should be informed of the reason.

Extensions to existing wiring, where they may be safely carried out, may conveniently be made in sheathed wiring, often run on the surface to avoid disturbance to decorations.

This surface wiring is a legitimate method, providing great care is taken to see that the cables are either protected from damage by means of a suitable metal cover, or else run in such a way that they can be clearly seen. A very neat job, with P.V.C. sheathed cable, can be carried out by running the cable along the top of a skirting board, and round a door frame, as depicted in Fig. 6.1. If the cable is subsequently painted to match the woodwork it will scarcely be noticed by the casual eye, yet it is sufficiently obvious to avoid the danger that someone will knock nails right through it.

A point where special care is necessary is where sheathed cable enters a floor. Here it is especially vulnerable. Half round or oval metal channelling should always be fitted at this point, to prevent accidental damage.

Surface-type fittings are usually employed in such work. These fittings have knockouts all round the box, and care must be taken (a) to knock out only the minimum area needed to accommodate the cable, (b) to see that all unused knockouts are left in position, to prevent the intrusion of dust, and (c) that the wires, as made off, are not pinched when the box is screwed to the wall.

When in doubt about the state of an old installation (and tracing wiring runs may be very difficult in old buildings) it is

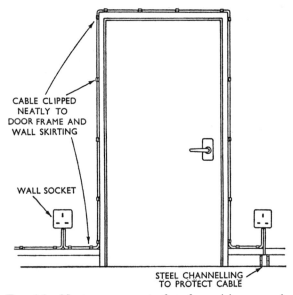

CABLE CLIPPED
NEATLY TO
DOOR FRAME AND
WALL SKIRTING

WALL SOCKET

STEEL CHANNELLING
TO PROTECT CABLE

FIG. 6.1. Neat arrangement of surface wiring around
the doorway and along skirting board, with protection
where the wire enters the floor. Bends must conform to
I.E.E. Regulations; see Table 7.

better to run the new circuits straight back to the fuseboard, and
then to ask the Area Electricity Board to connect them up.   It
is desirable that the Board should undertake the responsibility of
letting the householder know that the old wiring has deteriorated
and possibly needs renewing.

Conversion to ring circuit

It is often possible to convert an old wiring system which is
still in good order into a ring system, but of course this can
only be done if the size of conductor originally used is sufficient
to satisfy the Regulations: i.e. it must not be less than
2.55 mm² (7/·029).

Table 7. Minimum internal radii of bends in cables for fixed wiring

Insulation	Finish	Overall diameter for flat twin cable across the widest part	Factor to be applied to overall diameter of cable to determine minimum internal radius of bend
Rubber or P.V.C.	Non-armoured	Not exceeding 10 mm	3
		Exceeding 10 mm but not exceeding 25 mm	4
		exceeding 25 mm	6

Abridged from I.E.E. Wiring Regulations, Table B1M, 14th edition.

Example. If a 1·5 mm² twin sheathed P.V.C. cable were used with a major diameter of 8 mm then:
minimum *internal* radius bend = 8 × 3 = 24 mm.

For example, suppose a house has a 2·55 mm² (7/·029) feed straight from the fuseboard to a 15-ampere socket-outlet in the sitting room, and another similar feed to another 15-ampere socket in the dining room (Fig. 6.2). If these two feeds can be clearly traced at the fuseboard, they can be taken as the two ends of a ring, and brought into one 30-ampere fuse at the fuseboard.

At the remote ends, surface wiring can be taken from the socket-outlet in one room, all round that room, to feed as many 13-ampere socket-outlets as desired, and then through the dividing wall into the other room, to feed further socket-outlets in that room, terminating at the second original 15-ampere socket-outlet position.

A problem often facing those called on to extend old installations is the need to provide an earth connection, when the original installation employed only two-pin socket-outlets, with

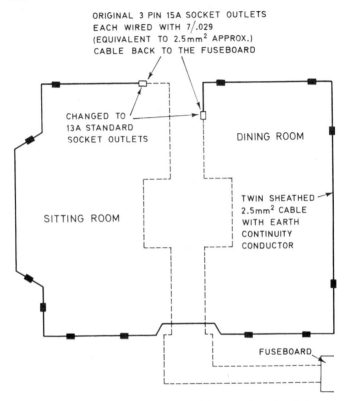

Fig. 6.2.   Conversion of old wiring to ring circuit by using the existing feeds to socket-outlets. *Note:* the existing wiring must be at least 2·5 mm² in size, and it is assumed that the original socket-outlets are correctly earthed with wire of 1·5 mm² minimum.

no earth.   In this case, there is no alternative, when installing the 13-ampere socket-outlets that must be used, to running an earth connection right back to the earthing point at the consumer's terminal.   The size of this conductor must be as laid down in the Regulations indicated earlier in this book, but it must not be smaller than 1·5 mm². The temptation to provide a local earth, near to the socket-outlet concerned, by making a connection to any nearby water pipe must be resisted, since the installation must never have more than one earthing point. If earth continuity conductors are added they must be insulated conductors, coloured green, and be properly clipped and protected throughout.

The tests that the electrician must make before commencing any work on an old installation (see chapter on testing) may show him that the system of supply is non-standard.

If he is engaged in rectifying a fault on the wiring it may be regarded as permissible to restore the faulty wiring to its original condition, with good workmanship and good materials, since the electrician cannot change the system of supply.

But if (as is often the case) non-standard wiring connections are found in an installation which is supplied on the standard 240-volt a.c. phase and neutral system, then the electrician is well advised not to restore the faulty non-standard wiring, but to put in standard connections (single-pole fusing, and proper earthing) on a new circuit installed in place of the old. He must not perpetuate incorrect wiring, which is basically unsafe and could give rise to serious troubles, including possibly fatal electrocution incidents.

An example of this aspect of obsolete installation problems was recently mentioned to the author by a contractor. His men went to the house of an elderly widow, who had written to him to say that the electric fire in her bathroom would not work. They found an antique, unguarded bare-element 2-kilowatt fire, plugged into a two-pin socket-outlet in the bathroom, obviously with no earth connection. Behind the socket, the rubber insulation on the v.r.i. wiring, installed in wooden troughing, had become so brittle that it had broken away, leaving the live wires bare. Some vibration had made them touch, and the fuse had blown. A nephew of the old lady had replaced the fuse with a much thicker wire, and this had also blown, burning his hand, so he left it alone.

The lady was most indignant when the contractor called on

her and said that it would be impossible to effect a simple repair, and that the socket-outlet should never have been fixed in the bathroom.

He was, of course, absolutely right in refusing to perpetuate a dangerous situation: but he learned later that a ' handyman ' had ' done the job ' for £1, and had simply taped up the insulation for a few inches, where the wire was accessible behind the old two-pin socket-outlet, and replaced the fuse. If the old lady had been electrocuted, he would have had much to answer for.

The contractor advised the Area Electricity Board that an unsafe installation existed, and they managed to convince the lady that rewiring was necessary.

Points about which to warn users of electrical installations

The users of an installation should be warned especially about the following points.

It is very unwise to use adaptors if at all possible to avoid them. They tend to give rise to radio and television troubles through loose contacts, and they may well become overloaded, and in consequence overheated, and possibly dangerous (see Fig. 6.3). They give rise to long lengths of flex, which may cause people to trip.

Never be a party to extending a flexible lead by simply jointing extra flex on to the end and making a taped joint. This can easily pull out and give rise to live wires lying on the carpet for children to touch, and the joint, simply being twisted, is never satisfactory and may itself overheat.

Avoid loose flex wherever possible since it is liable to trip people up or to give rise to trouble through being broken or frayed by being stepped on, and it should never be run under carpets or linoleum, since any damage that is occurring to it will not be seen.

Never agree to running an extension by stapling flex on to a skirting board. Flex is not suitable for this type of installation as it has no protection against mechanical damage.

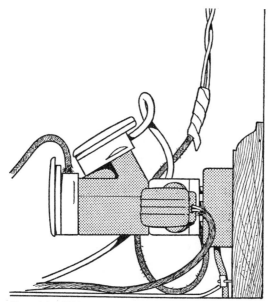

FIG. 6.3. This arrangement is to be avoided. This illustrates a mass of adaptors, which generally give rise to overheating, interference on radio and television, and the possibility of danger through tripping over flexible wires.

TEMPORARY WIRING

An electrician is often called on to rig up a temporary installation.

He should study the relevant section of the Wiring Regulations. In these Regulations, 'Temporary' is defined as referring to wiring not expected to be in use for more than three months.

Briefly, some of the more important points to be observed include the requirement that all temporary installations shall be dismantled as soon as they are no longer required, and in any case shall be completely overhauled at three-monthly intervals.

Every temporary installation must be provided with protection against excess current (normally by means of fuses) and with a switch or other device that disconnects *all phases or poles of the supply* (Fig. 6.4). Equipment that has been used on temporary installations, particularly those for outdoor use, should be thoroughly checked before being used again; corrosion may have rendered some items unsafe.

In a temporary installation no sub-circuit to which bayonet-type lampholders are connected may be loaded to more than 1000 watts, and the all-insulated lampholders that must be used should be fitted with a skirt. Except in private houses, temporary electrical installations must be in the charge of a competent person, whose name and address must be clearly shown, close to the main switch.

Apart from these special points, all temporary installations must be properly tested and must have the correct values of insulation resistance, earth continuity, and correctness of polarity (that is, the switches must be in the phase wire and not in the neutral, and socket-outlets must be connected the right way round) exactly as these requirements apply to permanent installations.

For the purposes for which most temporary installations are required, P.V.C. sheathed and insulated cable is usually suitable, but care must always be taken to ensure that temporary wiring is not inadvertently moved by other people so that, for example, wires lay in contact with a hot-steam pipe, or encounter similar hazards.

Stage lighting

A special case of temporary wiring often encountered relates to wiring for theatrical purposes in public halls.

If the supply is to be taken from 13-ampere socket-outlets (one of which is adequate for 3 kilowatts of lighting—thirty 100-watt lamps), care must be taken that double-pole isolating switches must be provided for the circuits connected to each separate socket-outlet.

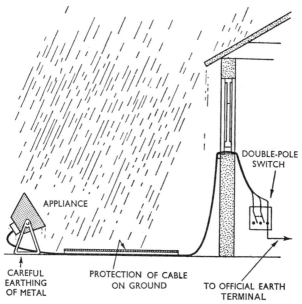

FIG. 6.4. Temporary wiring needs double-pole isolation.

Dimmers

Dimming of stage lighting is often required. Dimmers using variable resistances are available, and must be of the rating needed for each circuit, otherwise they will be overloaded and could become dangerously hot. The easiest method of providing for dimmers is to install an additional socket-outlet in the circuit, but to wire it in series with the phase wire and arrange for it to be short-circuited by a switch. The circuit is shown in Fig. 6.5.

Floodlight and spotlight connections

When supplying floodlights and powerful spotlights, the proper method is to terminate the main wiring 2 metres or more away from the floodlamp and then to feed the lamp, via the socket-outlet, with special heat-resistant cable.

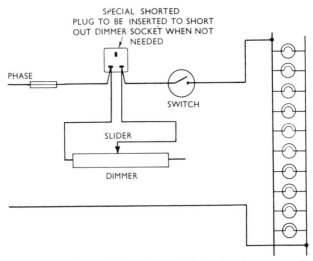

FIG. 6.5. The provision of an additional socket, normally shorted out by a shorted plug top, so that a dimmer can be inserted when required, as in a village-hall wiring system where stage lighting is occasionally needed.

Temporary outdoor wiring

Outdoor wiring for such purposes as floodlighting must be carried out with especial care, since driving rain may well penetrate any of the fittings, and give rise to danger of shock or short-circuits and blown fuses.

Extreme care in earthing every metal part of every floodlight or switch is essential. Nothing should be taken for granted—a check should be made with a testing instrument (see chapter on testing) to make certain all metal parts are properly earthed. Temporary earth connections to nearby pipes or other ironwork must not be used. The earth system must be continuous back to the earth point of the installation from which the supply is taken.

The switches used on temporary outdoor installations (as well as themselves being earthed) must be of the double-pole type. When assembling the cables, the entry holes in the switches and other appliances (such as the floodlamps themselves, or fuse-boards) should either be provided with weatherproof glands, or else carefully filled with the proper type of semi-plastic compound supplied by fittings manufacturers for this purpose, to prevent the ingress of moisture.

Where temporary outdoor cabling runs on the ground, it should be protected against damage by being covered with planking or some similar form of protection. Otherwise persons treading on the cable may drive sharp chippings through the insulation. It is always better to suspend the cable overhead, if at all possible.

7

TESTING ELECTRICAL
INSTALLATIONS

TESTING electrical installations can be considered from three
aspects: first there is the preliminary internal testing that must
be carried out by the electrician when an installation (or an
addition to an installation) is completed, and before it is made
alive; secondly, there are the official tests that are carried out
by the Electricity Supply Authorities before the installation is
connected to the mains; and finally there is the testing necessary
to find faults, or to ascertain the condition of an old installation.

Equipment needed

The basic instruments needed for testing and checking are
illustrated in Fig. 7.1. They comprise:

  (i) A universal test meter.

  (ii) A bell and battery set for tracing wires.

  (iii) A ' Megger ', combined with an earth loop continuity
      tester.

The universal test meter is a device whereby a single scale
can be read volts, amperes and ohms, by adjusting a knob with
appropriate markings. An instrument of this kind may be
acquired for about £30–40, and is the electrician's most valuable
tool. It must be capable of reading up to 500 volts a.c. or d.c.,
and the resistance range should be capable of reading down to
less than one ohm.

The resistance range on such meters is operated by means of
a small dry battery, inserted into the instrument in a similar
fashion to that employed in portable transistorised radio receivers.
To allow for variations in battery voltage, an adjusting knob is

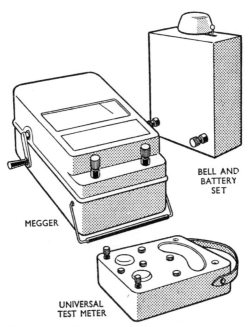

BELL AND
BATTERY
SET

MEGGER

UNIVERSAL
TEST METER

Fig. 7.1. The basic instruments needed for
testing and checking: the universal test meter,
the bell and battery set, and the ' Megger '.

provided. When the two leads from the instrument are clipped
together, obviously the resistance between them is practically
zero, and the adjusting knob is moved until the needle reads
zero. This adjustment should be carried out before every set
of resistance tests is undertaken.

For rapid checking of circuit connections, a bell and battery
set is extremely useful. Two torch batteries are connected to a
bell, and the assembly is connected to two probes or clip leads,
so that when the leads are joined together the circuit will be
completed and the bell will ring. A long lead will enable circuits
in all parts of a domestic installation to be checked out rapidly,
or ' rung out '.

It must be remembered that a ' ringing out ' test does not prove that the circuits are properly insulated, either between conductors or to earth, but only that there is a continuous conductor path from one point to another.

The ' Megger ' is a patented instrument which takes the form of a hand-driven generator that provides a voltage of 500 volts at the terminals.   It is used for measuring the insulation resistance of the installation.

The ' universal ' type of instrument, mentioned earlier, is entirely unsuitable for insulation testing, except for rough preliminary checks.   Such an instrument relies on a 2-volt battery, and one can imagine many parts of an electrical installation where bad workmanship or defective fittings or appliances have resulted in two bare wires, phase and neutral, being wrongly situated, and so lying within a hair's breadth of each other.   This gap will still show perfect insulation between them if a testing instrument using only 2 volts is applied, and the result will be misleading and a dangerous situation on the installation may not be revealed. But the 500 volts output of the ' Megger ' will break down such a gap, and the fault will be revealed.

The ' Megger ' has a scale that reads in thousands of ohms or in megohms (millions of ohms), and it is so arranged that once the turning of the handle has reached a minimum speed, no increase in speed will affect the reading.

Some types of ' Megger ' have a second instrument incorporated in the same case.   This instrument measures the impedance of the earth loop at any point in the installation.

With alternating current, as mentioned earlier, there are factors concerning the passage of current through a circuit other than pure resistance.   Where coils are concerned, the electromagnetic effect may mean that there is greater opposition to the passage of the current than that due to resistance.   The resulting combined opposition to the passage of current is called impedance, a term applicable to a.c. circuits only.

The impedance of the earth loop—that is, of all the conductors used to carry earth current from any one point on the installation to the general mass of earth—includes the resistance of the earth conductors in the installation, the resistance of the earth spike or other earth connection to the general mass of earth, and the electromagnetic effects (which may arise in any part of this circuit) mentioned earlier.

In the section on earthing, in Chapter 3, we have seen that this earth loop impedance must not be greater than a certain value. To check that the earth loop is below this impedance, a suitable instrument (which may be incorporated with the insulation-testing ' Megger ') must be used.

PRELIMINARY TESTING

All preliminary testing is of course carried out before the main fuses have been inserted.

The first test is a simple continuity test to ensure that all connections have been properly made. The bell set (Fig. 7.2)

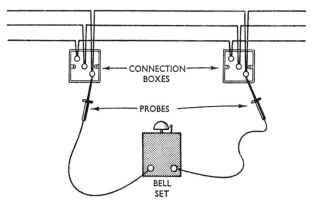

FIG. 7.2. A continuity test using the bell set.

can be used for this purpose, and also to check the proper connection of the switches, thermostats, time switches and other devices, to ensure that they are all on the ' live ' or phase side of the circuit. This can be tested by checking continuity from the neutral connection of the circuit being tested, at the fuseboard right through the thermostat, switch, or other interrupting device, making sure that the switch breaks the phase wire and not the neutral wire.

Next there is the question of polarity—socket-outlets having their connections made the right way round. On the ordinary 13-ampere fused plug socket-outlet, looking at the face of the socket-outlet, the live connection must be on the right, the neutral on the left and the earth at the top. A simple continuity check from each socket back to the phase fuse will ensure that this is correct (see Fig. 7.3).

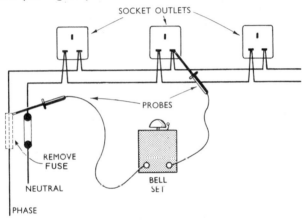

FIG. 7.3. A polarity test with the bell set.

The next step is to check earth continuity.

For this purpose, an *approximate* check, to satisfy the electrician that no gross errors have occurred, can be made by means of the universal testing instrument, arranged on its ohm-reading scale.

It will be recalled on the section on earthing that all exposed metal that can possibly become connected to a live circuit must be effectively earthed in such a way that there is resistance not greater than 0·5 ohm (or 1 ohm if the earth continuity conductor is of copper or aluminium) between the metal and the official earth point.

With one lead of the testing instrument on the earth point, and the other arranged as a probe that can be attached to all parts of the fixed appliances, or the portable equipment plugged into the socket-outlets, the earth resistance can be checked with the universal instrument (Fig. 7.4).

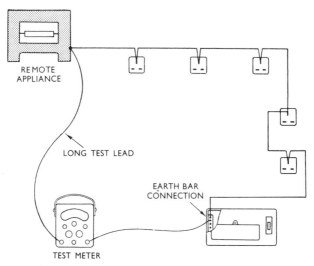

FIG. 7.4. Preliminary test of earth continuity resistance.

However, this cannot be taken as the full, official test. The reason for this again hinges on the fact that the universal instrument only has a 2-volt battery. Suppose an earth connection was badly made, so that the wires were simply touching each other, very lightly. This would mean that a 2-volt battery would show a good connection, but if a heavy current should pass through this circuit, the connection would obviously not be good enough: arcing and ultimate melting of the surfaces in contact would occur, with consequent fire danger.

In fact, the Regulations specify that when testing the earth conductor, alternating current of a magnitude approaching one and a half times the rating of the circuit under test shall be used, with a maximum of 25 amperes. As mentioned above, only a properly designed instrument can provide a test current of an appropriate value to make sure that any slightest defects in the earth continuity system are observed and can be detected (see Fig. 7.5).

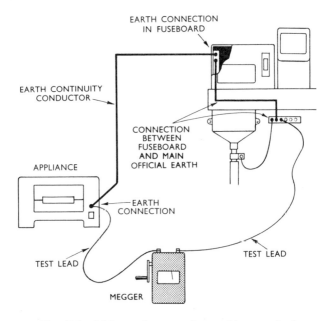

Fig. 7.5. 'Megger' test on the earthing continuity.

Insulation test

This test ensures that the insulation throughout the whole installation has not been damaged in any way, and for ordinary medium-voltage circuits, that is up to 650 volts, 3-phase, the test has to be carried out, according to the Regulations, with a direct current voltage not less than twice that which will be normally applied to the installation, although it may not exceed 500 volts.

The figure of 500 volts is that which is usually used, with the aid of the ' Megger '.

Again, the universal type of instrument would not be suitable, even using its resistance scale. If, for example, the wire running through a conduit had been strained over a sharp edge incorrectly left at the end of a tube, the bare conductor might be within half a thousandth of an inch of the earthed metal, and yet the 2-volt output of the instrument would not break down this gap and reveal the defect.

The insulation resistance is measured on each circuit by closing all switches on all appliances in circuit, and with the neutral connection disconnected (Fig. 7.6). Under these conditions the circuit will be complete throughout the phase wire, the switch, the appliance, and the neutral wire back to the switchboard.

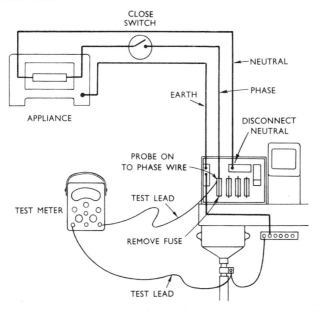

FIG. 7.6.   Insulation test circuit.

The universal tester again may be used to provide a rough check. One lead should be clipped to the official earth point (or for a rough preliminary test) to a water pipe or other convenient earth, and the other lead to the phase wire. The reading on the ohm scale of the instrument should be of the order of 1 or 2 megohms. This test is only suitable for finding major errors, such as the live wire firmly touching the earth connection in a fitting or connection box.

But it must be emphasised that the only conclusive and official test is that carried out with the 500-volt ' Megger '.

The bare minimum insulation resistance acceptable under the regulations is one megohm—1,000,000 ohms, applying to the complete installation. This means that when all the phase wires at the fuseboard are connected together and to the testing instrument, all switches closed, all appliances inserted in the circuit, all neutral wires being left in the air, and the other end of the ' Megger ' is connected to earth, then there is a minimum of 1,000,000 ohms between the whole of the installation taken together, and earth. A higher value should always be aimed at, and a good installation might well have an insulation resistance of well over 5 megohms, or 5,000,000 ohms.

A second insulation test should be carried out between conductors (see Fig. 7.7); for the purpose of this test all lamps and appliances are removed, or isolated by opening their local switch, and the test instruments' leads connected to the phase or ' live ' conductor and the neutral conductor, the minimum reading being 1 megohm.

If for the purpose of either of the above tests, equipment is removed, then it should be tested in a similar manner separately, and in this case a minimum reading of half a megohm is permissible.

OFFICIAL TESTING

The Area Electricity Board or other Electricity Supply Authority will test the installation for insulation resistance, for earth continuity, for earth loop impedance back to the earthed neutral on the supply transformer, for correct connection of the final earthing

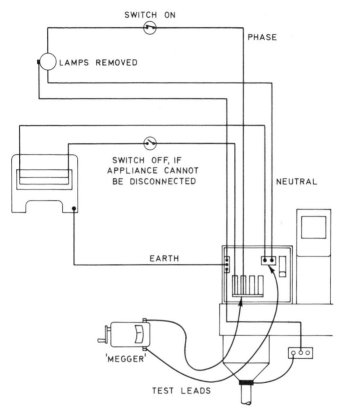

SWITCH ON

PHASE

LAMPS REMOVED

SWITCH OFF, IF
APPLIANCE CANNOT
BE DISCONNECTED

NEUTRAL

EARTH

'MEGGER'

TEST LEADS

FIG. 7.7. Insulation test between conductors.

point, and for adequate fusing. They will also check the quality
of the wiring, and if an earth leakage circuit-breaker has been
installed, in areas where no official earth point is possible, they
will check the operation of this device, and the earth resistance of
the electrode used.

They are not concerned with the internal connections of the
installation itself and it is not their duty to see that the proper
lamps light when the switch is closed, or that appliances such as

water heaters and the like, installed by the electrician, operate
correctly. They are, however, concerned with the safety aspect
of ensuring that all socket-outlets are connected up the right way
round, and this point will therefore be checked by the Electricity
Board's engineers.

They will also check that there are no socket-outlets in bathrooms, and that other safety measures have been observed.

If off-peak storage heating circuits are installed, a check will
be made to ensure that these circuits are all terminated directly
on the storage heaters, and that no other socket-outlets or other
connections exist on these circuits.

Tracing faults

Suppose now that the electrician's own preliminary tests have
revealed a fault on the system.

With the aid of his bell set, and his universal meter, he can
usually track down the fault quite quickly if he observes the
simple principle of sectionalisation.

Let us suppose that the fault is an insulation fault—that
means that the whole installation shows that the phase wire is in
effect connected to earth, and therefore does not have the required
insulation resistance of at least 1,000,000 ohms with respect to
earth.

The circuits comprising the installation can easily be separated
out at the main fuseboard. Taking one circuit at a time (the
fuses, of course, still remaining withdrawn) the electrician can
disconnect the neutral wires and thus both ends of the circuit
are clear of any other connection. Then, with all the switches
closed and appliances connected, he checks each circuit under
these conditions, until he finds one (or more) on which there is a
fault (see Fig. 7.8).

Concentrating on this circuit (all others being healthy) first
the appliances may be disconnected, one by one, until a possible
faulty appliance shows up. If no appliance is faulty then proceed
as follows:

Assume for the moment that there is only one fault in the circuit. The electrician then goes to the first disconnection point

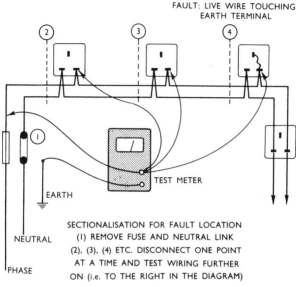

FAULT: LIVE WIRE TOUCHING
EARTH TERMINAL

TEST METER

EARTH

NEUTRAL

PHASE

SECTIONALISATION FOR FAULT LOCATION
(1) REMOVE FUSE AND NEUTRAL LINK
(2), (3), (4) ETC. DISCONNECT ONE POINT
AT A TIME AND TEST WIRING FURTHER
ON (i.e. TO THE RIGHT IN THE DIAGRAM)

FIG. 7.8. Principle of sectionalisation when testing for faults.

on this circuit (which might be a joint in a box in the conduit run, or a connection box on the sheathed cable run), and disconnects both wires.

He returns to the fuseboard and once again checks both the phase and neutral wire for insulation to earth. Suppose he now finds that they are both 'good', and the fault has thus been removed by this disconnection. It is obviously beyond the point of disconnection.

He next transfers his testing instrument to the first joint box, which he has already opened, and proceeds further to the next joint box or to a switch, the next break point on the circuit, and disconnects the wires in this second connection box.

Testing again, he finds that the fault is either cleared or not cleared. If it is cleared, he proceeds further down the circuit. If it is not cleared, then obviously it lies in the section between his testing point (at this first disconnection box) and the further point at which he has broken the circuit.

Suppose the fault *is* cleared, then he must proceed further and go beyond the switch (or second connection point) which may perhaps bring him to some fittings or socket-outlets. These must be methodically disconnected, one by one, testing after each disconnection, until the faulty unit is isolated. It must then be inspected to find where the fault lies.

One of the most common causes of faults in domestic installations is that the wiring behind a socket-outlet or a switch has been incorrectly made off, so that either too much bare conductor exists, and is touching the earthed metal or the neutral wire, or, on the other hand, the switch or other fitting may be incorrectly assembled, possibly so that two wires are incorrectly inserted into one terminal (see Fig. 7.9).

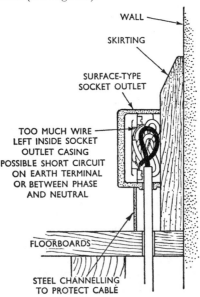

WALL

SKIRTING

SURFACE-TYPE
SOCKET OUTLET

TOO MUCH WIRE
LEFT INSIDE SOCKET
OUTLET CASING
POSSIBLE SHORT CIRCUIT
ON EARTH TERMINAL
OR BETWEEN PHASE
AND NEUTRAL

FLOORBOARDS

STEEL CHANNELLING
TO PROTECT CABLE

Fig. 7.9. Common causes of faults on
electrical systems.

Suppose the fault has been found to be in a run of cable. If the installation is carried out in conduit, it will not be very difficult to pull out the cable in that section and inspect it, and the fault will probably soon be found. It may well be due to the insulation being damaged as the cable was drawn into the conduit. This should not have happened.

If the installation is carried out in sheathed wiring embedded in plaster, then the electrician faces the job of breaking out the section containing the fault and replacing it with new wire. It is unwise to attempt to locate the fault and to patch it up. New cable must be used.

Up to now it has been assumed that the fault is one of bad insulation. There are, however, two other kinds of faults.

First, there is a short-circuit (Fig. 7.10). Both the neutral and the phase wires may remain well insulated from earth, but are short-circuited to each other.

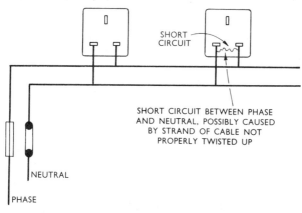

FIG. 7.10. Testing for a short-circuit.

In the majority of cases this is due to incorrect connections in fuses, switches or fittings. It is unlikely that the wires within a conduit, or inside the sheath on a sheathed cable, have come into contact with each other without at the same time going down to earth, although this type of fault could not necessarily always be ruled out. A short-circuit could occur if severe mechanical damage has occurred to sheathed cable, perhaps under a floor, where for example, a workman from another trade, such as a plumber fitting water pipes or a gas fitter has inadvertently severely manhandled the cable.

The short-circuit can be isolated by the same methodical sectionalising test methods as those outlined above.

Another type of fault is the open-circuit (Fig. 7.11). Here

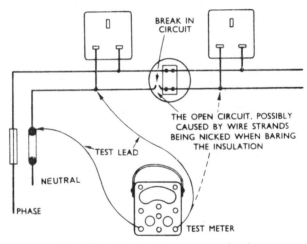

FIG. 7.11. Testing for an open-circuit.

again, in this case where there is no circuit between two points, the fault is most likely to lie in a switch or other fitting. There have been cases where open-circuits have arisen when fittings have been incorrectly made off, and the electrician, roughly baring the ends of the wire, has nicked through all the strands, and then when the tension comes on the ' tail ' which has been inserted into a switch or socket-outlet or some other fitting as the unit is screwed together, the weakened wires break away, leaving an open-circuit.

Cables that have been badly kinked before installation could give rise to open-circuits, as the kinking may have broken the copper conductors.

The open-circuit may not be so easy to find, under certain circumstances, as the other types of fault, but with the aid of a long test lead, it is not difficult for the electrician to parallel each installed wire by an external lead across the gap between, say, two junction boxes, or the main fuseboard and a fitting, and if a complete circuit is obtained in this way, he can shorten his test lead until he finds the section or fitting in which there is an open-circuit (see Fig. 7.12).

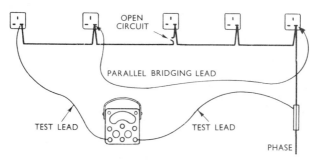

FIG. 7.12. Locating an open-circuit by parallelling sections of the wiring with a long test lead.

TYPICAL FAULTS

Through the courtesy of the National Inspection Council for Electrical Installation Contracting, it is possible to mention here a few of the most commonly found faults in electrical installations.

Incorrect system of fusing

Where the normal supplies of phase and neutral are concerned, inspectors have frequently found double-pole fusing, which is incorrect. This is most often found in a final sub-circuit where there is a sub-circuit distribution board.

Proximity of different phases

As explained at the beginning of this book, nowadays domestic and small business installations are frequently fed by a 3-phase system, in which a voltage of 415 volts exists between wires connected to different phases. The Regulations state that in general all the conductors in one room should be connected to the same phase. There is an exception that allows points between which a voltage exceeding 250 volts is present to exist in the same room if they are 2 metres or more apart, but as mentioned earlier where storage heaters are installed (of the type in which a fan is used to assist in the heat output and to provide a measure of control), very often it has been found that conductors of two different phases are used near together, since the storage heater is supplied independently from one circuit which may be connected to one phase, and the local control circuit for the fan is connected to another, which is not part of the off-peak system, since the fan may be needed to increase the output when the off-peak power is not available.

Insufficient protection for sheathed wiring

It is frequently found that when sheathed wiring is out of sight, it is also out of the electrician's mind, in the sense that he has not provided any protection at all. It is just as important that sheathed wiring should be protected from mechanical damage in such places as lofts and cellars, which are infrequently used, as it is in cases where the wiring is obviously visible (see Fig. 7.13).

Conduit installation troubles

Insufficient attention has frequently been found to be given to the filing away of sharp edges on the ends of conduit piping, and the lack of the provision of bushes. This means that all cables drawn through this particular piping may well be abraded, and liable to subsequent failure.

Insufficient attention has frequently occurred in regard to the protection of conduits, ducts, and trunking systems against the entry of water.

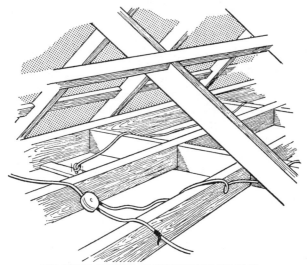

DEPRECATED PRACTICE OF UNSUPPORTED SHEATHED
WIRING IN LOFT, WITH JUNCTION BOX UNFIXED

FIG. 7.13. Bad wiring in lofts and cellars is sometimes
found, with the wiring unsupported and the junction
boxes unsecured.

Overcrowding of cables in conduits and trunking

Notes in this book have indicated that no more wires than
those laid down in the various Regulations should be accommo-
dated in a given circuit, and if these figures are exceeded there
may be trouble due to overheating and possible failure, and in
any case the cables will have to be derated. (Used at a lower
current rating than normal.)

Incorrect cable for heated appliances

Heat-resistant insulated cable should always be used for
connections to immersion heaters, thermal storage heaters and
indeed any appliance that gets hot. It has often been found that
ordinary P.V.C. insulated cable is employed.

Omission of any identification at the fuseboard

If the circuits are not identified and the types of fuses that are appropriate for each circuit clearly stated, it will be much more difficult to put right any trouble of any kind that may arise on the installation, now or in the future.

Failure to realise that certain locations require the use of flameproof or intrinsically safe equipment

In places where inflammable liquids are stored, or where, for example, the gas bottles used for welding, or for domestic gas purposes in connection with caravans and the like are located, properly designed flameproof equipment and wiring is necessary.

Insufficient attention to the bonding of all metal-work to earth

Every piece of metal in any way associated with an electrical appliance should be bonded to earth, and it is often found that some part of an installation is omitted in this connection. Examples include the catenary wire used to support an overhead wire running outdoors.

Omission of protective shield or skirt to lampholder of bathroom, in lighting pendant or fittings (see page 118)

GENERAL NOTE ON TESTING OLD INSTALLATIONS

The electrician may be called on to rectify a fault on old wiring in a location with which he is not familiar.

He must not start by assuming that the supply system is the usual single-phase and neutral 240-volt a.c. system. As mentioned earlier in this book, several other systems are still in use in small areas of Britain, and in other countries it is unlikely that he will find the same system in use as that which is generally standardised in Britain.

Voltages may be different, direct current may be used, neither supply wire may be at near earth potential in the same way as the neutral, and the frequency may be different.

The first test, therefore, should be to find out the system in use.

The nameplate on the meter, plus the information given on any lamp that may be in use, will provide a useful starting point. The meter will show if the system is a.c. or d.c., and the frequency employed, and probably the voltage as well, and in any case the lamp will show the voltage.

But the universal test-instrument should be applied to check the voltage from each supply wire, separately, to earth.

It should always be assumed that the system is wired up wrongly: never take it for granted that single-pole fusing (as standard on modern British installations) is used or, that single-pole switches are placed in the phase conductor, or that the neutral wire is in fact at or near earth potential, or that any earth connection at all does in fact exist.

Test records

The electrician should keep a record of all tests, and this record should be dated and a copy left with the installation. It will greatly assist anyone working on the installations at a later date.

Testing an installation after fire or water damage

If a fire has occurred in some part of a house, or if, for example, flooding has taken place, or if a tank in a loft has overflowed, a check should be initiated immediately before any current is used.

The main switches on the fuseboard should be opened at once, and the ' Megger ' should be applied to each circuit to make two insulation tests. First, when the fuses are removed, access can be obtained to the phase end of each circuit and the neutral connections can be taken out one by one, and with all appliances disconnected but the switches on the circuits closed, an insulation test can be carried out between phase and neutral on each circuit. Then a similar insulation test is carried out between each conductor and earth.

With plastic wiring, heat may have caused considerable damage to the wiring and major renewal operations will have to be commenced.   On the other hand, water damage will not have affected the insulation itself, but may have given rise to pockets of water in socket-outlet boxes, switches and other fittings.   This means that each of these may be opened and dried out carefully, and for this purpose an ordinary hair dryer fed from some circuit in another part of the house which is in good order, may conveniently be used.   It is probable that at least one circuit may have escaped major damage.

8

MISCELLANEOUS ASPECTS OF INSTALLATION PRACTICE

Outdoor wiring

Apart from underground wiring connections between buildings (which may best be carried out by means of mineral-insulated copper-sheathed conductor with an outer covering of plastic, properly protected by means of bricks or concrete slabs), outdoor wiring should employ a catenary, or suspended system (Fig. 8.1).

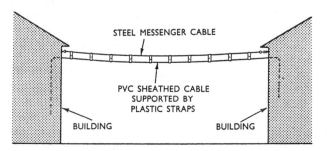

FIG. 8.1. Catenary wiring system for outdoor work.

There are two methods of catenary suspension. In one method, a special cable is employed, using a chlorosulphonated poly-ethylene (c.s.p.) sheathed cable with a built-in steel wire for suspension purposes. In the second method, a separate steel wire is employed, and the special outdoor cable is suspended from it by means of straps made from plastic material in ring or tape form.

It is permissible to span a gap of 3 metres between adjacent buildings by means of a span of P.V.C. sheathed and insulated cable, carefully cleated at each end to ensure that its own weight, and possible movement in the wind, will not cause the cable to be damaged at the cleats.

Bell, television and telephone wiring

It should be clearly noted that wiring for the purposes of bell circuits, telephone circuits, television and radio circuits does not come within the scope of the I.E.E. Wiring Regulations, except in so far as the Regulations state that this wiring must be kept entirely separate from any wiring connected to circuits which are themselves joined to the mains. This is the first principle to be observed in regard to what we may now call auxiliary circuits.

Bell wiring

Bell wiring calls for little comment. Most bells or chimes are supplied from a bell transformer which must be properly fused with a 1-ampere fuse on the high voltage side. The first test should ensure that both windings are continuous and the second test should ensure that the insulation between the 240-volt side, and the 8- or 14-volt side is in good order (see Fig. 8.2).

Bell-circuit wiring is usually carried out in twin plastic flex, which may well be run in plastic conduit beneath the plaster, or may be neatly tacked with insulated staples on the surface in the case of existing installations. Joints in such wiring should preferably be soldered and taped, since it is desirable to make sure that there is minimum resistance at any jointing point, but ordinary mains-type screw connectors may of course be used.

Telephone wiring

The Post Office (in Britain) does not normally permit the electrician or contractor to install wiring for telephones, although this procedure is not unknown, and certainly takes place where large blocks of flats or offices are concerned. What they are anxious to stress is that they would like to be advised of new telephone connections that are to be fitted, as early as possible, and they are willing to provide polythene plastic ducting to be built into the house, and to run to a suitable point outside, so

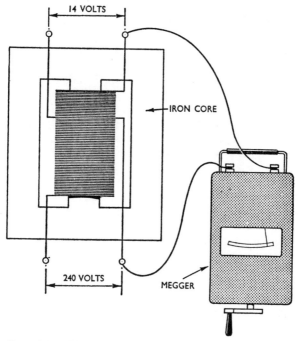

FIG. 8.2. The bell transformer, checking insulation between high voltage and low voltage sides.

that telephone wiring may be installed by their own staff when the house is completed.

If this procedure is adopted, the telephone wiring can be concealed as unobtrusively as the power wiring, and the appearance of unsightly telephone wires, stapled on top of the skirting board and round the door frames, can be avoided.

Internal telephone facilities

Internal telephone facilities are sometimes needed, and the wiring of these can be installed at the same time as the mains wiring, but care must be taken to ensure that the right kind of wiring is used. Many ' intercom ' circuits use what is called multi-core cable, that is, cable having perhaps ten cores if there are to be, say, eight instruments.

If there is to be more than a single pair of telephone instruments, giving a single link, then two wires are not generally sufficient, since (without the costly and complicated dial-type system) with, say, three instruments, telephone A has to be switched through to either telephones B or C, and if, for example, it is switched through to B, then telephone C has no way of getting in touch with A, since he presumably would not wish to go to telephone A first and change over the switch and then return and talk over the circuit.

It is possible by using a Yaxley type switch, commonly found as a wave-change switch in radio receivers, and by employing four wires instead of two to connect all instruments together, to be able to switch as required and allow any instrument to call any other instrument.

Television and radio circuits

It is becoming increasingly common for television and V.H.F. aerial down-lead circuits to be installed as part of the wiring of a building, and to terminate on high-frequency sockets which are themselves mounted on plates that fit standard wiring boxes, so that they may be sunk flush into the wall, enabling the television set aerial lead to be plugged in neatly.

Low-loss television cable may be used for two purposes: for the television connections, and for the V.H.F. radio connections for F.M. radio reception. It is common to install such wiring below the plaster in plastic conduit, so that it can be pulled out if trouble develops.

Unlike mains voltage wiring, however, there is no technical reason why this wiring, which is usually plastic covered, could not be installed directly in the plaster, but if so there is always the possibility that it may be damaged by nails driven into the wall. It will then become very difficult to replace, and any fault could necessitate breaking away plaster walls and subsequent redecoration.

There is a most important point to be watched in this connection. The method sometimes adopted by electricians, unaware of high-frequency problems, is to bring the lead from the aerial on the chimney into the loft or other similar area, and then to join on to it leads running to high-frequency sockets, in for example, the dining room, the sitting room, and possibly a bedroom as well. This means that the aerial lead has connected to it one socket which is in use for television reception and two other sockets which are not in use, and this frequently causes what is called, in electronic circles, a ' mis-match ', so that reception is impaired.

To avoid this trouble, the correct method is to bring the lead from the aerial down to the point most likely to be used regularly, such as the sitting room, and then to run the television cable onwards from there to the next room, and from there to the third or other plug points that are to be provided (see Fig. 8.3). At the termination in the sitting room a special high-frequency switch can be provided to switch in the additional television cable length into, say, the dining room, or else a neatly arranged lead can be left with a male socket on the end which can be plugged into the wall socket in place of the connection to the television set, and which has the effect of extending the aerial down-lead in series, into the dining room, and (with the same arrangement) on to a bedroom or other receiver point. In this way, the best reception will be obtained without troubles due to mis-matching.

Audio-frequency (sound) circuits

In some installations enthusiasts for recording on tape (perhaps in connection with the making of sound films), may like to have facilities whereby one room can be used as a studio and the output from the microphone and amplifier taken to other rooms where recording can be carried out without the noise of the instruments disturbing the studio atmosphere.

This facility can be provided very easily if it is foreseen during the installation work. All that is needed is to use the same type of V.H.F. television cable as used for the television circuit itself, and to provide links between the rooms, terminating in each

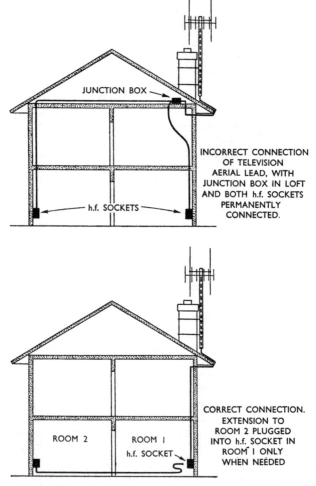

JUNCTION BOX

INCORRECT CONNECTION
OF TELEVISION
AERIAL LEAD, WITH
JUNCTION BOX IN LOFT
AND BOTH h.f. SOCKETS
PERMANENTLY
CONNECTED.

h.f. SOCKETS

CORRECT CONNECTION.
EXTENSION TO
ROOM 2 PLUGGED
INTO h.f. SOCKET IN
ROOM 1 ONLY
WHEN NEEDED

ROOM 2

ROOM 1

h.f. SOCKET

FIG. 8.3.   Incorrect and correct connections of television
aerial leads to high-frequency sockets in various rooms in
the house.

case on a flush-type high-frequency socket-outlet inset in the wall, so that microphone or loudspeaker circuits can be plugged in as required without running very long leads (which may pick up hum or give rise to attenuation problems) through passages and under doors.

Motor circuits

Until the last decade most small motors, such as those used in domestic premises and in small workshops, had to be provided with starting devices, but nowadays quite large motors, up to 3·5 kW or above, can in some cases be started by simply switching them on to the mains.

The types of motor used in such domestic devices as washing machines, vacuum cleaners, refrigerators, power drills, and the like, do not involve any special problems for the electrician. However, for motors slightly larger than those just mentioned, that is, approaching 750 W and larger (such as those used for lathes in small workshops), there is one factor that needs to be taken into account.

When a motor starts, it may well take ten or twelve times the current it draws when operating normally. This current rush at starting is of brief duration, but nevertheless may blow fuses unnecessarily, since the installation will not be harmed, nor the wiring overheated, by this excess current of very brief duration. To give an example, a 750 W motor of the 1-phase type at full load will take just over 3 amperes per phase, but when starting it may take considerably more current than this and the makers recommend that a 10-ampere fuse should be used on the fuse-board concerned.

Motors that have to start very frequently may give rise to difficulties as the excess current during the starting period heats up the fuse more and more, and ultimately it may blow during the next starting current, but not because of any defect in the installation.

One method of avoiding this difficulty is to install a motor starting unit, which is usually available from the manufacturer of the motor, and comprises a pushbutton-operated starting switch. It is usually equipped with a special overload device to prevent damage to the motor or to the installation. These devices often take the form of a thermal overload. A small heating element, suitably proportioned, is connected into the motor circuit, and operates a bimetal strip in much the same way as in the case of a thermostat mentioned earlier, and the bimetal strip when it operates trips out the switch.

For domestic and small workshop applications, single-phase motors are the most commonly used. They present no problems in regard to their connection to the supply.

For larger drives, the 3-phase motor requires a special 3-phase socket, and a proper 3-phase isolation switch must be provided, even if the starting arrangements are incorporated within the machine to be driven.

Transformers

The transformer is a most useful static device, with no moving parts and therefore no need for maintenance, used to change one voltage to another. Basically, it has remained unchanged since it was first developed by Faraday in 1831.

The transformer consists of a ring of iron wire or iron stampings made from thin plate, arranged in the form of a ring (Fig. 8.4). On one side is a winding having, let us say, a thousand turns, and on the other side a winding having, say, one hundred turns.

If the thousand-turn winding is now connected to a mains supply of alternating current, then a voltage will appear on the hundred-turn winding which is exactly one-tenth of that applied to the other side. The voltage can be stepped up or down at will, providing the coils are suitable for an application at the voltage desired.

The most common example of the transformer found in domestic use is the bell transformer, usually giving 8 or 14 volts from the 240-volt supply. In this case, it would obviously be very wrong to connect 240-volt mains to the 8-volt terminal, as not only would the insulation of the 8-volt winding be insufficient for 240 volts, but in addition the dangerous voltage of 7200 volts

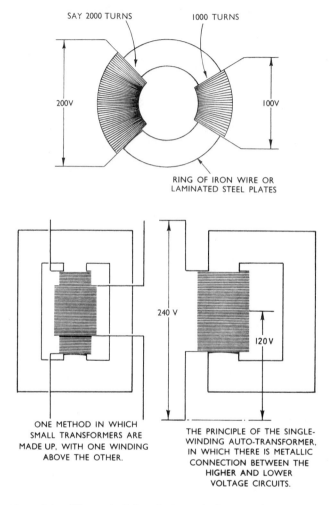

SAY 2000 TURNS

1000 TURNS

200V

100V

RING OF IRON WIRE OR
LAMINATED STEEL PLATES

240 V

120V

ONE METHOD IN WHICH
SMALL TRANSFORMERS ARE
MADE UP, WITH ONE WINDING
ABOVE THE OTHER.

THE PRINCIPLE OF THE SINGLE-
WINDING AUTO-TRANSFORMER,
IN WHICH THERE IS METALLIC
CONNECTION BETWEEN THE
HIGHER AND LOWER
VOLTAGE CIRCUITS.

Fig. 8.4. The principle of the transformer: the two-
winding transformer and the auto-transformer, which is not
permitted for normal use in domestic premises.

—30 times as much as normal—would be produced on the 240-volt winding, and this too would flashover to earth and destroy itself since its insulation would also be insufficient.

There are regulations concerning transformers which insist that the insulation between the two windings should be of at least as high a value as the insulation of the primary or 240-volt winding to earth. This prevents the high voltage from penetrating to the low-voltage side.

There are, however, certain types of transformer known as auto-transformers, which must not be used for domestic purposes, although they have many applications in industry. In this type of transformer there is a single winding arranged on one side, as it were, of the iron ring, and the full mains voltage is applied across the winding. A tapping is taken from it, at, say, half-way down, to provide half the main voltage. This means that there is physical connection between the 120-volt circuit and the 240-volt circuit, and a breakdown in the winding (which does happen from time to time on small transformers) could result in 240 volts being applied to the 120-volt circuit. This is the reason why the auto-transformer is not permitted for use in domestic premises.

Continental equipment

The marking of the wires connecting continental equipment to the mains is often different from that used in Britain, and care must be taken to ensure that the earth wire is correctly ascertained. Some continental machinery uses white earth wires, and many domestic appliances manufactured on the Continent have no earth connection at all. In such cases, the two-core flex should therefore be removed and a three-core flex substituted, but there a further problem arises. Within the device itself—say, for example, a food mixer—it may not always be possible at first glance to see where to attach an earth connection in such a way that it ensures that all metal parts that can be touched are connected properly to the earth wire. This means some care and thought on the part of the electrician, and perhaps he may need to arrange some bonding wires within the appliance to make certain that all metal parts of all kinds within the appliance are in fact joined together and to earth. However, the appliance may be of the double-insulated type (see page 18), and this work is then unnecessary.

Cupboard door switches

The electrician may be asked to provide an arrangement whereby when a cupboard door is opened a light within it is lit up. This can be done by means of a normally off switch specially provided for this purpose. These switches have a protruding knob which is so arranged that it may be pressed by the back of the cupboard door as the door closes, and this action holds the switch open. As the door is opened the knob springs out and closes the circuit. These switches can be inserted into the frame of the door in a hole specially made, or they may be mounted inside the frame with a wooden block on the door carefully arranged to press on the knob and open the switch as the door closes.

Connections to gas appliances and oil-fired central-heating plant

The electrician may well need to provide a supply for the equipment that is associated with central-heating equipment, either for lighting up the flame when a thermostat determines when it should be lit, or for increasing water flow in a central-heating water system circuit.

The supply to such devices may be made by normal socket-outlet, but the cable used must be of the asbestos-insulated heat-resistant type.

In certain installations that are somewhat larger than those normally found on domestic premises, it may be necessary to use flameproof switches and other fittings in the room where the gas- or oil-heated boiler is situated. Consultation with the manufacturers will decide this matter.

Connections to under-floor electric heating

For bungalows especially, under-floor electric heating is frequently employed.

This form of heating may be carried out in several ways, but basically they all consist of electric wires buried in the floor and covered by a layer of cement. Some systems employ plastic-coated mineral-insulated copper-sheathed cable, which may be safely operated at high temperatures, others employ special heating wires simply immersed in the concrete, while what is probably the best system uses a conduit buried in the cement of the floor, and withdrawable heating cables.

For a room of 5 metres by 4 metres a floor heating loading of about 3 kilowatts is necessary, and this is better supplied by means of a separate feed run directly back to the fuseboard. This is because there is the need to insert a thermostat in the circuit, to prevent undue consumption of current, and this would mean a wiring complication if the floor heating was supplied from the normal ring circuit.

In any case, such supplies may well be taken at off-peak periods, so that a separate feed is automatically needed.

The actual designing and installation of a floor-heating system is not likely to be undertaken by a beginner, as it requires specialist knowledge, and in any case must be carried out over a considerable period in close collaboration with the builder. Such a system can very rarely be installed in any but new buildings.

Warm-air central heating and air conditioning

Some houses are equipped with ducted air systems, so that air is warmed up at a central point (or at several points) by electric heaters, with fans to control the flow of air.

In providing supplies to these heaters, the only point the electrician has to observe is to ensure that the cables are of adequate size (since some heating elements exceed 3 kilowatts in capacity) and that the necessary thermostat connections, as required by the makers, are incorporated into the wiring layout.

In many houses in America and in some in Britain, complete air conditioning is employed. This means that the air taken into the sealed, double-glazed and fully insulated interior of the house is cleaned, humidified if necessary, and heated in winter or cooled in summer, the air-conditioning plant being provided with both heating and refrigerating units.

Some of these air conditioners have complex thermostat and humidity-controlling devices, which need extensive wiring runs; and since the load on many of them is quite high—12 kilowatts is common for an ordinary three-bedroomed house in America—obviously special large current-carrying mains and appropriate fuses are needed.

Dimmers

To dim a lighting circuit is not easy because the only way in which the light can be gradually lowered from full brightness to blackout is by continuously lowering the voltage applied to the lamps. A commonly used method in the theatres and dance halls is to insert a variable resistance between the mains and the lamp circuits to be dimmed.

This resistance obviously carries the whole current of the lighting system, and so will develop heat. Moreover, until recently most resistance dimmers of this type were fairly bulky, and could not therefore be easily incorporated into the lighting circuits of, say, an ordinary lounge or dining room.

Nowadays, devices have been developed of a size not very much larger than a socket-outlet, which can be safely buried in the wall, and are arranged so that the heat is safely dissipated.

However, even more modern methods of dimming are already in use in theatres and are also available for domestic service. In these devices, a large-size transistor is used. This transistor, known as a thyristor, or silicon-controlled rectifier, in effect blocks the current for part of each cycle of alternation, the amount of blockage being controlled by the application of a control voltage to one of the electrodes of the thyristor. This means a small auxiliary supply and a variable resistor such as those used on the volume control of a radio set, and therefore the device has to have certain auxiliary electronic components which are obviously costly at this stage. Such a device is inserted in the lighting circuit and allows for full control, without the problem of heat loss, and in relatively small bulk.

Delay switches

In buildings where there are a number of flats with access by stairways instead of lifts, delay switches are sometimes fitted, particularly on the Continent, to allow for the lights to be switched on when entering the building at basement level, and for them to remain on for a given period of perhaps five minutes. They then switch themselves off to avoid current waste in lighting up the staircases and passages during the night, when no light is needed.

These delay switches take several forms. In some the pressure on the switch winds up a small spring, which then unwinds over a period and switches off the circuit. In another form a pneumatic piston is provided within the switch, which is lowered into its cylinder against the air pressure by the operation of switching on, and then as the air gradually escapes through a controlled orifice, the piston rises with the help of a spring and switches off the lamp. These devices can be purchased from most switch manufacturers.

Burglar-alarm circuits

There are several patent burglar-alarm systems on the market, but many of them have the disadvantage that being widely advertised the burglars themselves are fully familiar with their requirements. The best system is undoubtedly one evolved specially for the installation concerned. Obviously all windows and doors need some kind of protection, and small radio-type switches will have to be installed on every door and window to operate if the door or window is opened. A circuit can be evolved whereby even if the burglar sees the wiring and cuts it, the alarm still operates. This system is arranged as shown in Fig. 8.5.

In this system each door or window is equipped with a switch similar to those used on cupboard doors to allow the light to light up if the door is opened, and basically the closing of this switch closes a circuit from a bell transformer through a bell and so gives the alarm. But if the wires are cut obviously no alarm is given.

Therefore two other features are introduced. A relay is

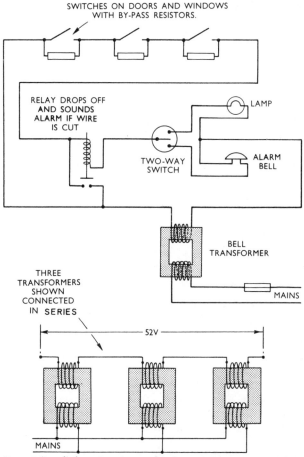

FIG. 8.5. A burglar-alarm circuit, using a relay, so that
cutting the wiring will also give an alarm.

provided, of the type used in telephone circuits, obtainable from
many of the secondhand radio dealers specialising in this type of
equipment, and a resistance is placed across the switch (a radio

resistance of something of the order of between 2 and 12 ohms is suitable if a number of burglar-alarm switches are connected in series), and then sufficient current flows to energise the relay but not to actuate the bell.

The contacts of the relay are connected across the burglar-alarm circuit so that if it is not energised the relay drops off and makes the contact and rings the bell, thus indicating that the wire has been broken either by a burglar or by some accident, which is of equal interest since it indicates that the burglar-alarm system needs overhaul.

A further refinement is to use a two-way switch to cancel the bell ringing and instead to light up a lamp, so that during the day-time hours, when doors and windows are constantly being opened, the flashing of the lamp will serve to indicate both that the burglar-alarm system is working and to remind the occupiers to change over the switch to the bell position when retiring.

If this system is built in at the time when the wiring is installed in the house, it will obviously give a much neater job and will remove the danger of damage to the wiring, but it is quite possible to make a neat job of fitting a burglar-alarm system of this kind by neatly running thin plastic wiring with insulated staples along skirtings and up the edges of door frames.

The burglar alarm itself may well have a bell situated outside the house to call the attention of the police or neighbours, and if so a bell designed for outdoor use is needed.

It may be found that the ordinary bell transformer, if used for this purpose, does not provide a sufficient voltage if there are long lengths of wire involved and a number of resistances in series, and the relay will not therefore be permanently energised, as it must be.

The simplest method to overcome this difficulty is to use two bell transformers in series, and it might even be necessary to employ three as shown in the diagram. If this is done, care must be taken to wire up the transformers properly, since if the connection is not correct the voltages, instead of adding up as they should, in a series connection, will be reduced since one or other of the transformers may be in opposition to the other at any given moment.

Trial and error with the aid of the universal testing instrument will show whether this connection has been properly carried out, but if the manufacturers' markings are relied upon and, say, the left-hand terminal of each transformer is regarded as the ' phase ' and the right-hand terminal as the ' neutral ' then by connecting phase and neutral in series, it is extremely likely that the voltages will add up correctly.

Photoelectric cell circuits may be used also for burglar alarms (Fig. 8.6).   A photoelectric cell is a device like a valve in a radio

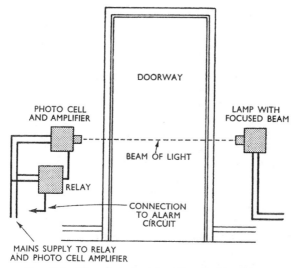

FIG. 8.6   The photoelectric cell and the wiring necessary.

set which conducts current when light is thrown upon it, or sometimes operates by ceasing to conduct when light is withdrawn. A beam from a lamp is focused by lenses across an aperture such as a doorway which is to be protected, and falls on to a photoelectric cell, the current from which is amplified by transistorised amplifiers fed from a mains circuit, and this current operates a relay which is normally held open. If the beam of light is interrupted by the passage of a person or other object, the relay falls off and the alarm circuit is connected.

A variant sometimes used is to employ an infra-red beam, that is to say a beam of radiant energy which cannot be seen (such as the heat energy that comes from a hot pipe which is not red hot) and this can operate a special type of electric cell.

The wiring for these devices follows the standard rules as regards its installation, but the actual connections are given by the makers of this type of equipment, since each type differs.

Baby-alarm circuits

One facility often provided is the baby-alarm circuit, so that a microphone can be placed beside the baby's cot in an upstairs room, and if the child cries it can be heard in the sitting room, dining room, or kitchen. For this method a small amplifier is needed and the system will use a microphone point or points in the room where the baby's cot may be expected to be situated, a central amplifier, and leads to small loudspeakers to be installed in such rooms as may be selected, for example the sitting room, dining room, and kitchen or possibly the parent's bedroom.

The first point concerns the microphone itself which will have to be of the moving-coil type, commonly employed for tape recording, since the crystal type (which is the cheapest) will not lend itself to the long extension leads involved in this system.

The microphone points may well take the form of flush sockets of the V.H.F. type, and to get the best results should be wired with television-type cable back to the central amplifier which will have running from it switched loudspeaker lines (which again are best run with television-type cable although since hum is not likely to be picked up on these wires, ordinary twin plastic cable can be used).

The same wiring rules apply as in other cases, which are that the wires are best run in plastic conduit beneath the plaster, but in any case must not have any contact with any type of circuit fed from the mains.

Emergency lighting

Although it is always hoped that the public electricity supply service will not be interrupted, nevertheless this does happen from time to time. Emergency lighting can be provided in ordinary domestic premises, with moderate cost, by using a trickle charger suitable for a car-type 12-volt battery, the battery itself, and a relay (see Fig. 8.7).

It is possible to purchase (often at electronic equipment shops) a relay which will remain permanently energised as long as its coil is connected to the 240-volt mains circuit. This relay

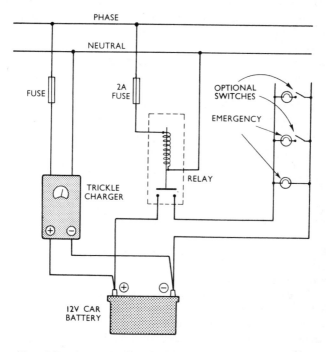

FIG. 8.7. An emergency lighting circuit, using a trickle-charged 12-volt automobile-type battery as the main source of supply.

should be properly fused on the mains side with a 2-ampere fuse, and should be enclosed to prevent damage.

The contacts, which remain permanently open when the relay is energised, may be connected to the battery and to a 12-volt lighting circuit run as required in the house. Since this is not mains wiring, it is not subject to the normal regulations, but may be run in any desired method, providing these wires are not brought into contact with the mains. However, twin plastic cable run in plastic conduit will be quite satisfactory, but surface wiring neatly cleated is of course permissible.

Obviously emergency lighting is not required everywhere, but one 36-watt car headlamp bulb in the sitting room, another in the kitchen and perhaps a 6-watt on the landing and a further 6-watt bulb in a lavatory may be regarded as sufficient to enable the life of the household to be carried on after a fashion.

When the relay drops off through mains failure, all these lamps will be lit. As mains failure is rare and in any case is usually for short duration, it may not matter if the lamps remain alight, even if all of them are not needed. In any case, the battery benefits by being discharged on occasion. If no failures occur for long periods, the battery may deteriorate.

This is no reason why a switch should not be provided for any or all of the lamps, but it may well happen that this switch is left in the off position and thus the effect of emergency lighting, in providing an immediate illumination on mains failure, will be lost, and people will have to grope for the switches; so that on the whole it is desirable to leave the lamps alight. When the mains supply is restored, the relay will automatically pick up and break the circuit, and the battery will at once become automatically charged up once more.

The type of relay obtained may not necessarily have contacts that will carry the whole current for the emergency lighting circuit if all the lamps are in use, and it may be necessary to employ a second relay, operated from the battery, with contacts of greater capacity. The first, or main failure relay, simply operating a battery circuit for the coil of the second relay, whose contacts will carry the whole of the main current. This depends on the type of relay obtained. The current for a 36-watt car headlamp bulb at 12 volts is 3 amperes and thus if two of these are in use plus two 6-watt lamps, 7 amperes will be needed, and not all relay contacts will carry this current for any length of time.

It is however possible that certain types of Post Office relays have a number of contacts, designed originally for closing a number of circuits at once, and these contacts can be paralleled up so that the current is shared between them and they are all working within their rating.

Electricity in the greenhouse and the garden

Electricity may be used in a greenhouse for heating, for seed propagation, for raising cuttings and for soil sterilisation, and many other purposes. It may also be used in the garden to drive an electrically operated lawnmower or hedgecutter.

Great care should be taken when installing socket-outlets in greenhouses where damp and humid conditions often prevail, to ensure that all fittings are of the weatherproof type, and that the greatest care is taken to ensure proper earthing, since an electric shock obtained under these conditions would be especially dangerous.

Conduit systems or mineral-insulated copper-sheathed cables with metallic fittings are the best for this purpose, and if an outdoor socket for the lawnmower is provided, again this must be carefully installed so that corrosion effects are minimised. Boxes with a removable screwed cover are especially suitable. Heavy galvanised conduit and galvanised boxes are perhaps the best solution, but failing this, a well-constructed box made of weatherproof material such as plastic or metal, properly earthed, should be made to contain the socket-outlet, and the box should be provided with some small ventilation holes covered by gauze to prevent the access of insects, so that condensation that takes place within it will not affect the electrical contacts. The conduit entries and all other orifices (except the condensation outlets) should be carefully plugged with semi-plastic compound, to keep out moisture.

INDEX